PEARSON
Physics
James S. Walker

Laboratory Manual

Christopher J. Chiaverina
New Trier High School
Winnetka, Illinois

Diane M. Riendeau
Deerfield High School
Deerfield, Illinois

PEARSON

Boston, Massachusetts   Chandler, Arizona   Glenview, Illinois   Upper Saddle River, New Jersey

Cover photograph: Victor de Schwanberg/Science Source
Cover designer: Ellen Granter
Cover production: 17th Street Studios

ISBN-13: 978-0-13-297840-8
ISBN-10: 0-13-297840-7
1 2 3 4 5 6 7 8 9 10 11—EBM—18 17 16 15 14 13

Contents

To the Teacher

Young people are, in many respects, much like scientists: They possess a natural curiosity about almost everything. By nurturing your students' innate inquisitiveness through exploration and experimentation, you, their teacher, have an opportunity to make them aware of the wonders that abound in nature, to instill in them an understanding and appreciation of the scientific principles operating all around them, and to equip them with the skills that will enable them to function effectively in the modern world. In essence, you have the power to turn your students' natural curiosity into scientific adventure.

While it's true that students can gain an understanding of science by watching, listening, and reading, science education research has shown that in order to better grasp both the content and methods of science, students must be given the opportunity to engage in the activities of scientists; that is, they must be allowed to directly interact with nature and formulate and test their own hypotheses. To this end, the activities in this manual have been designed to allow students to emulate the work of scientists by providing opportunities for scientific inquiry.

About the Lab Manual

This laboratory manual has been written to accompany *Pearson Physics* by James S. Walker and consists of 75 laboratory activities. The manual contains essentially three types of activities: qualitative, inquiry-based explorations; quantitative experiments; and performance tasks. As an introduction to a concept, the qualitative explorations are meant to be student-centered and engaging. Many of the qualitative activities are presented in the form of a collection of introductory experiences relating to a single concept or principle. The activities, which may be done in any order, are arranged in numbered stations around the room. Manipulatives at each station invite exploration and discovery; the book provides suggestions for using them and posits thought-provoking questions that guide further inquiry. Students draw upon their existing knowledge when responding to these questions.

Qualitative labs serve several important functions. First and foremost, they introduce concepts through hands-on investigation. Using tangible materials in the context of guided inquiry, students are given an opportunity to interact with nature. As a result of direct contact with phenomena, students observe relationships and begin to acquire conceptual understanding. Qualitative labs are intended to permit students to make "discoveries" by allowing them ask "what if?" In addition, these lab experiences encourage collaboration, mitigate science anxiety, and often reveal students' preconceptions.

As the name implies, quantitative laboratory activities involve the use of numbers, equations, and graphs. The activities are meant to extend and amplify the material introduced in the qualitative explorations. In performing these labs, students make measurements, collect and analyze data, arrive at conclusions, and communicate results. Questions at the end of each activity require that students focus on the meaning of the outcome of the activity, why conclusions were drawn, and sources of error that may have affected experimental results.

Performance tasks are open-ended experiments that are designed to determine a student's ability to use his or her knowledge to solve a problem. Performed at the completion of a unit of study, performance tasks serve as a means of summative evaluation, for they offer insights into a student's level of conceptual understanding.

Students begin a performance task by designing a procedure to experimentally determine an unknown quantity specified in the problem. Before carrying out the experiment, students write a concise procedure, describing any measurements that are to be made and indicating how the measured quantities would be used to determine the unknown quantity. They then identify the equipment they will need. The teacher supplies students with one or two pieces of apparatus; however, students may request additional pieces of equipment. After completing the experiment and arriving at an answer to the problem, students list possible sources of experimental error.

The activities selected for inclusion in the manual are of both the "high-tech" and "low-tech" varieties. Generally speaking, the high-tech activities require commercial apparatus such as sensors, interfaces, specialized software, and computers. The use of such equipment greatly enhances data collection, analysis, and display. Information not readily obtained with traditional, noncomputerized instrumentation, such as real-time data regarding the position, velocity, and acceleration of a moving object, are possible using computer-assisted data acquisition and display.

Low-tech activities, which often may be performed with readily available materials commonly found in the physics storeroom, home, or hardware store, provide a low-cost way for students to have meaningful interactions with phenomena. Low-tech activities have the added advantage of being transparent. Since the equipment used to perform them is uncomplicated, the physical principles they are used to illustrate are demonstrated in the simplest possible way.

An equipment list, estimated time for setup and performance of an experiment, and safety considerations, all in blue type, accompany each lab. The times required for setup, which include the gathering of equipment and "time in lab," are only estimates and will vary. In some cases, students may have to analyze data collected in the laboratory outside class as homework. The safety notes focus on precautions that should be taken when students perform a particular experiment. Margin notes for the teacher offer suggestions for making experiments run more smoothly and efficiently and provide sources for apparatus and materials not found in the typical physics storeroom, among other recommendations.

Since this manual contains more experiments than can most likely be performed in a one-year high school physics course, it will be up to the teacher to decide which experiments are appropriate. The inclusion of additional experiments in this manual is meant to allow for flexibility. Experiments chosen by the teacher will depend on availability of equipment and laboratory time, as well as applicability to the material being taught.

Safety in the Laboratory

The experiments in this book have been carefully designed to minimize the risk of injury. However, safety is the responsibility of both student and teacher. The following rules are essential for keeping your students safe in the laboratory. They are written directly to the student. Please ensure that your students follow these guidelines.

Note: There is a student Safety Contract in the Student Edition. Please make sure each student understands and signs it.

Pre-Lab Preparation

- Read the entire procedure before you begin. When in doubt about a procedure, ask your teacher.
- Do only assigned experiments. Do not work on an experiment unless your teacher is present and has given you permission to do so.
- Get approval from your teacher for any student-designed procedure before attempting it.
- Know the location of the fire extinguisher and the fire blanket, and how to use them.
- Know the location of emergency exits and escape routes. Do not block walkways with furniture.
- Keep your work area orderly and free of personal belongings such as coats and backpacks.

Safe In-Lab Practices

General Safety

- Listen to and follow all of your teacher's instructions.
  - ⚠ **Caution:** *Immediately report any accident, no matter how minor, to your teacher.*

Eye Safety

- Wear goggles at all times when working in the laboratory—goggles are designed to protect your eyes from injury.
- Never look directly at the Sun through any optical device. Do not use direct sunlight to illuminate a microscope.
- Avoid wearing contact lenses when the experiment involves chemicals. If contact lenses must be worn, then wear eye-cup safety goggles over them.

Clothing Safety

- Avoid wearing bulky or loose-fitting clothing.
- Remove dangling jewelry.
- Wear closed-toe shoes at all times in the laboratory.

Thermal Safety

- Protect your clothing and hair from sources of heat. Tie back long hair and roll up loose sleeves when working in the laboratory.
- Use extreme caution when working with any type of heating device.
- Do not handle hot glassware or equipment. You can prevent burns by being aware that hot and cold equipment can look exactly the same.
  - ⚠ **Caution:** *If you are burned, immediately run cold water over the burned area for several minutes until the pain is reduced. Cooling helps the burn heal. Ask a classmate to notify your teacher.*

Chemical Safety

- Never taste any chemical used in the laboratory, including food products that are the subject of an investigation. Treat all items as though they are contaminated with unknown chemicals that may be toxic.
- Keep all food and drink that is not part of an experiment out of the laboratory. Do not eat, drink, or chew gum in the laboratory.
- Wear safety goggles, an apron, and gloves when working with corrosive chemicals.
- Report any chemical spills immediately to your teacher. Follow your teacher's instructions for cleaning up spills. Warn other students about the identity and location of spilled chemicals.
- To reduce danger, waste, and cleanup, always use the minimal amount of any chemical specified for an experiment.
  - ⚠ **Caution:** *If a corrosive chemical gets on your skin or clothing, immediately wash the affected area with cold, running water for several minutes. Ask a classmate to notify your teacher.*

Sharp Object Safety

- Don't use chipped or cracked glassware. Don't handle broken glass. If glassware breaks, tell your teacher and nearby classmates. Discard broken glass as instructed by your teacher.

  ⚠ **Caution:** *If you receive a minor cut, allow it to bleed for a short time, then wash the injured area under cold, running water. Ask a classmate to notify your teacher. More serious cuts or puncture wounds require immediate medical attention.*

Electrical Safety

- Recognize that the danger of an electrical shock is greater in the presence of water. Keep electrical appliances away from sinks and faucets to minimize the risk of electrical shock. Be careful not to spill water or other liquids in the vicinity of an electrical appliance.

- Do not place electrical cords in such a way that they become trip hazards.

- Do not let cords hang off tables in such a way that could lead to the equipment being pulled off the table accidentally.

- Always be sure that any piece of electrical equipment is off before plugging it in and before unplugging it.

- Have your teacher inspect and approve all electrical circuits before they are used.

  ⚠ **Caution:** *If you spill water near an electrical appliance, stand back, notify your teacher, and warn other students in the area.*

Post-Lab Procedures

- Always follow your teacher's directions for cleanup and disposal. Dispose of used chemicals in a way that protects you, your classmates, and the environment.

- Wash your hands thoroughly with soap and water before leaving the laboratory.

One or more of the following safety symbols will appear in every experiment. Take appropriate precautions.

SAFETY SYMBOLS

 Eye Safety Wear safety goggles at all times.

 Clothing Protection Wear a lab coat or apron when using corrosive chemicals or chemicals that can stain clothing.

 Skin Protection Wear plastic gloves when using chemicals that can irritate or stain your skin.

 Broken Glass Do not use chipped or cracked glassware. Do not heat the bottom of a test tube.

 Open Flame Tie back hair and loose clothing. Never reach across a lit burner.

 Flammable Substance Do not have a flame near flammable materials.

 Corrosive Substance Wear safety goggles, an apron, and gloves when working with corrosive chemicals.

 Poison Never taste a chemical in the laboratory.

 Fume Avoid inhaling substances that can irritate your respiratory system.

 Thermal Burn Do not touch hot glassware or equipment.

 Electrical Equipment Keep electrical equipment away from water or other liquids.

 Sharp Object Avoid puncture wounds by using scissors and other sharp objects only as intended.

 Disposal Dispose of chemicals and other supplies only as directed.

 Hand Washing Wash your hands thoroughly with soap and water.

Chapter 1 Lab   Introduction to Physics Exploration

Purpose

In this lab, you will explore physical phenomena that will be studied in depth during the course of the year.

Materials

Appropriate materials will be found at each station.

Discussion

Physics is a branch of science whose goal is an understanding of the most basic principles and laws governing the interaction of matter and energy. The scope of physics extends from the smallest subatomic particles to the entire observable universe.

   This collection of laboratory activities is meant to provide you with an overview of topics you will be studying this year. These topics include mechanics, sound, light, electricity, and magnetism. While the principles and concepts associated with these terms may be foreign to you now, by the time you complete this course, you will not only have an understanding of their meaning, you will see how they play a role in your everyday life.

Procedure

Station 1: Vibrational Energy

Strike the end of a tuning fork on the rubber pad provided or on the heel of your shoe. Barely touch the surface of the water with the vibrating ends of the tuning fork. What do you observe?

The tuning fork will cause the water to vibrate and may even spray the

water out of the container.

Do you think the vibrating tuning fork tines possess energy? How do you know?

The tuning fork does possess energy due to the motion of the tines. This

energy normally produces the sound waves that we hear. When the tines

are placed in water, this same energy is transferred to the water molecules,

making them move.

Time to Set Up: 1 h
Time in Lab: 1 h
Qualitative Lab

This lab is intended to be done the first day or two of class to set the stage for the school year. Students should be encouraged to answer the questions without fear of getting the answers wrong. Resist the temptation to correct students or provide answers. The lab activities can be done in any order.

Equipment
Tuning fork (low frequency works best), mallet or rubber actuator, plastic cup filled with water

Safety
Avoid using a glass container because the tuning fork might shatter it.

Equipment
Coat hanger, about 1.5-m-long string (optional: cooling rack, silverware, or barbecue grate)

Station 2: Sound through String

Wrap the center of a length of string around the hook of a metal coat hanger a number of times. Wrap one end of the string around your left index finger and the other end of the string around your right index finger. Hold your hands out so the coat hanger hangs freely. Let the coat hanger strike the edge of a desk or chair. Describe the sound produced.

Students will hear a quiet, tinny sound.

Now gently put the tips of your index fingers in the openings of your ears and once again allow the freely hanging coat hanger to strike a hard object. How does the sound you hear this time compare to the sound heard when your fingers were not in your ears?

Students' answers will vary; however, students should notice that the sound
is louder and lower pitched.

How was the sound produced in each case?

In both cases, the sound was produced by knocking the hanger against
an object.

How did the sound reach your ears in each case?

In the first case, the sound traveled through the air, and in the second case
it traveled through the string. The string transmits low frequencies more
effectively than the air.

Equipment
Two pieces of paraffin wax, piece of aluminum foil, rubber band or glue

Assembly
Cut the aluminum foil slightly smaller than the wax blocks so that it does not hang over the edge. Make a foil sandwich on paraffin "bread." Make sure that the foil is not visible. Rubber band or glue the sandwich together.

Station 3: Paraffin Puzzle

View the pair of paraffin blocks from the side. Notice that the upper block is brighter than the bottom block. Turn the blocks upside down so the upper block is now on the bottom, and vice versa. Which block is brighter now?

Students should find that the top block is always brighter than the bottom block.

How do you explain your observation?

Students do not know that the foil is between the blocks. The reason for the
difference in brightness is that the light coming from the top cannot pass
into the lower block; instead, it is reflected back into the top block of wax.

Equipment
White coffee cup, sheet of black construction paper

Station 4: Black Hole

Look into the cup through the hole in the black card. Based on what you see, predict the color of the inside of the cup.

Students' answers will vary. They may predict that the inside of the cup is
black or white.

Lift the card off the cup to check your prediction. Do you think the color of the inside of the cup has any bearing on the apparent color of the hole in the card? Explain your answer.

The hole will appear blacker than the surrounding black paper. The hole

approximates a blackbody, an object that is an ideal absorber of light. Light

entering the hole can escape only after undergoing so many reflections

inside the cup that almost no light escapes, even though the surface of the

cup is a good reflector.

Station 5: Colored Shadows
Describe the appearance of the screen. (Notice that the screen is illuminated with red, green, and blue lights.) Now place a pencil fairly close to the screen. Adjust the pencil's distance from the screen until you see three distinct colors. What colors do you see?

Students should see a red, a green, and a blue shadow of the pencil.

Adjust the pencil's distance until you can see six distinct colors. What colors do you see?

Students should see red, green, blue, cyan, magenta, and yellow shadows.

How do you think these colors are produced?

The combination of red, green, and blue light produces white. Blocking

blue light allows only red and green to reach the screen. These overlapping

colors produce yellow. When red light is blocked, the remaining green and

blue lights produce blue-green or cyan. Magenta is produced if only red

light and blue light illuminate the screen.

Station 6: Egg Spin
Place the eggs on the table. Handle the eggs very carefully so that they do not break. Spin the egg marked with an "X." Now stop the egg with your index finger placed on its center. Immediately after the egg stops, remove your hand. Describe what happens.

Students should notice that the egg marked "X" will resume spinning after

they stop it and then let go.

Now spin the egg marked with an "O." Again stop the egg with your index finger and then quickly release it. Describe what happens this time.

Students should notice that the egg marked "O" remains at rest after they

stop it and let go.

Assembly
The construction paper should be the blackest available. The paper should completely cover the mouth of the cup. Make a hole about the diameter of a pencil in the center of the construction paper. Place the construction paper on top of the cup.

Equipment
Red, green, and blue lights; white screen

Safety
If using incandescent bulbs, they will become hot.

Assembly
Red, green, and blue flood lamps and colored compact fluorescent bulbs work well. The screen may be paper or another white surface. Place the lights approximately 50 cm from the screen. Line up the lights as closely together as possible. The screen should appear approximately white with all three bulbs illuminating it.

Equipment
Hard-boiled and fresh eggs

Assembly
Mark fresh eggs with an "X," hard-boiled eggs with an "O." Have extra eggs available in case they get broken during the lab.

Why do you think the two eggs behave the way they do?

When a spinning hard-boiled egg is stopped, it will remain at rest. When the shell of a spinning fresh egg is stopped, the egg's liquid core remains in motion. When the shell is released, the egg begins spinning again.

Station 7: Tug of War

Equipment
Two constant-velocity cars, string, 200 g mass, batteries

Assembly
Tie a string from the back end of one of the cars to the other so that they can pull in opposite directions. Place fresh batteries in both cars.

Note that the two constant-velocity cars are connected by a piece of string and are arranged to pull in opposite directions. Turn on both cars simultaneously and let them pull against each other. Who wins the tug of war?

Ideally, neither car should "win." The cars should remain stationary.

Now turn off the cars and place a 200 g mass in the car that lost the first tug of war. Turn the cars on again, and observe what happens. Which car wins the tug of war now?

The car with the 200 g mass should win the tug of war.

Explain the results of both tugs of war.

If the two cars happen to push on the table with equal force prior to adding the mass, there will be no winner. Adding mass to one car increases friction between that car's tires and the table top, which increases the force the car exerts on the surface of the table.

Station 8: Fickle Friction

Equipment
Two identical textbooks

Place two books of the same size face up on the table. Open both books and overlap their back covers by about 10 cm. Shuffle the pages of the books together (as you would playing cards) until you reach the front covers. It is not necessary to overlap every page. Keeping the books on the table, try to separate them by pulling horizontally. Now rotate the books so that the covers are perpendicular to the table. Stand the books on the table and once again try to pull them apart. Jostle the books a bit while pulling on them. Did you succeed in pulling the books apart in either orientation? If so, which one(s)?

Students should be able to separate the books only when their covers are perpendicular to the table.

Why do you suppose this is so?

Students will not be able to separate the books when their covers are parallel to the table because of the frictional force acting between pages. This frictional force is proportional to the normal force (due to gravity) acting on the books' pages. When the book covers are perpendicular to the table, the normal forces, and the frictional forces they produce, nearly vanish.

Station 9: Magnetic Braking ⚠️

Drop a small piece of chalk into a length of copper tubing. Now drop a strong magnet into the tube. How do their motions compare?

The students should find that the chalk traveled quickly down the pipe

while the magnet traveled much more slowly.

How do you explain the behavior of the two objects?

Students' answers will vary.

Repeat the experiment, but this time use a nonmetallic tube with dimensions similar to those of the copper tube. Describe what happens.

Both the magnet and the chalk should travel quickly through the pipe.

Explain your observations.

As the magnet falls through the copper tube, a current is induced in the

walls of the tube, producing a magnetic field that opposes the motion

of the magnet. The nonmagnetic chalk does not produce an opposing

magnetic field. Because PVC is not a conductor, no opposing field will be

produced and the magnet's motion will be unimpeded.

Equipment
Copper tube, PVC pipe, chalk, neodymium magnet

Assembly
The copper and PVC tubes should be between 0.5 and 1 m long and have a large enough diameter to allow the magnet to pass through them.

Safety
Students should take care to avoid pinching their skin between the neodymium magnet and other metal surfaces.

Station 10: Fluid Attraction

Rub the balloon on your hair. Bring the balloon near a thin stream of tap water. What happens to the stream as the balloon approaches it?

The stream of water should be pulled toward the balloon.

Why did the water behave this way?

Water molecules are electrically neutral, but polar. When a charged object is

brought near water, the side of the water molecules with a charge opposite

to that of the charged object, due to their proximity, will be attracted with

a stronger force.

Do you think all liquids would behave similarly?

Students' answers will vary.

Equipment
Balloon, thin stream of water

Assembly
A rubber rod can replace the balloon if students have latex allergies. It is important to use a narrow stream of water. If the stream is too thick, the relatively small electrostatic force will not deflect the water.

Name _____ Period _____ Date _____

Chapter 1: Introduction to Physics • Scientific Inquiry

Chapter 1 Lab   Line-Following Car Exploration

Purpose
In this lab, you will use scientific inquiry to design, perform, and report on an experiment using the Line-Following car.

Required Equipment/Supplies
- line-following car set equipment based on the experimental designs
- posterboard, butcher paper, or whiteboard
- markers

Discussion
A line follower is a car that comes with a marker and a mat. When you draw a line on the mat, the car will follow it. How does it work? Scientists strive to answer questions like these. Using scientific methods of inquiry, work with your peers to discover what factors affect the operation of the car.

Procedure

Part A
As a class, discuss the variables you could test regarding operation of the line-following car. Ask yourself, what could I change to see if that affects the way the car works? List these items below.

Variables might include: color of pen, thickness of the line, curvature of the line, color of the paper beneath the line, type of pen used to draw the line.

Part B
1. With the help of your instructor, choose one variable for your group to investigate.
2. Develop a hypothesis about how changing your variable affects the line-following car's performance. Write your hypothesis here.

   An example hypothesis might be, "The car will only follow a line drawn with the black marker and not the blue or green one."

3. Design an experiment that tests how changing this variable affects the performance of the line-following car.
4. Write a "step by step" procedure.

   Emphasize that the procedure needs to be written so that another group could repeat the experiment based only on the written procedure. An example procedure follows:

Time to Set Up: <1 h
Time in Lab: 1 h
Qualitative Lab

Line-following cars, available from online toy marketers, are often sold under the brand name "Line Chaserz." The cars are designed to optically sense the location of a line and follow it. Assuming the role of scientists, students will pick their own variable, write a hypothesis, design an experiment to test the hypothesis, and present their results to the rest of the class. Students should be allowed to explore use of the cars before your class discussion.

Check the procedure for uncontrolled variables and safety considerations before you allow the students to proceed.

a. Use a blue, green, and black marker to draw three lines on the provided mat. The lines should be the same thickness.

b. Place the car at the beginning of one line and let it go.

c. Note whether the car follows the line.

d. Repeat for all three lines and record data in the data table.

5. Ask your instructor to approve your procedure BEFORE you begin experimentation.

Part C

1. In the space below, prepare a data table in which to record your data.
2. Follow your procedure (from Part B) and record the data.

Students' data tables will vary. They might simply be charts indicating the color or thickness of the line and whether or not the car followed the line.

_____

_____

_____

_____

_____

_____

_____

_____

Part D

Using your data, draw a conclusion regarding your hypothesis from Part B. Write your conclusion below.

An example conclusion might say, "We found that our hypothesis was wrong. The car followed not only the black line but also the blue and green lines."

Part E

Prepare a poster to present your findings to the class. Be sure to include the following:

- Your hypothesis
- List of controlled variables
- Your data table
- Your conclusion
- Suggestions for further study

Have each group present its findings and answer questions from the remainder of the class.

All members of the group should participate in the making of the poster and be ready to explain the findings to the class.

Chapter 1: Introduction to Physics • Graphing in Physics

Chapter 1 Lab   Graphical Analysis

Purpose

In the lab, you will collect, represent, and analyze data with accuracy.

Required Equipment/Supplies

- digital scales
- small plastic container
- small washers
- large washers
- prepared cubes
- centimeter ruler
- liquids of known density
- graduated cylinders
- disposable pipettes
- paper towels
- graph paper

Discussion

Taking data is an important skill. However, what you do with the data is equally important. This lab requires that you take data at three stations. Graphing data often helps a scientist see how variables are related. The goal of this lab is to practice taking data and finding relationships between variables using graphical analysis.

Procedure

There are three different activities in this lab. The order in which you perform them is not important. Please move to an open station when you finish collecting data from your starting station and continue in this fashion until you complete all three activities.

Station 1: Washers: Mass versus Number of Washers

1. Zero the scale.

2. Place the empty container on the scale. DO NOT REZERO THE SCALE!

3. Add the small washers to the scale, one at a time, and note the scale reading after adding each one. Record your data below.

4. Repeat steps 1–3 using the larger washers.

Number of washers in container	Small washers	Larger washers
	Mass (g)	Mass (g)
1		
2		
3		
4		

Time to Set Up: 1 h
Time in Lab: 1 h
Quantitative Lab

This lab is designed to allow students the opportunity to take data and produce three different types of graphs. The data from Station 1 result in a line graph. The importance of the slope and y-intercept of the graph is also introduced. In analyzing the data from Station 2, students produce a parabolic graph. The data from Station 3 produce an inverse graph.

It is best to have two setups of each station to reduce the number of students at any one station at a time.

Equipment
Digital scale, small plastic container, large washers, small washers

It is important that the students zero the scale before placing the container on it.

Equipment

Prepared cubes, centimeter ruler

Assembly

Prepare 4 cubes. You can make them by gluing sugar cubes or dice together, using 1, 4, 9, and 16 cubes or dice.

Remind students that surface area is length × width

Station 2: Cubes: Surface Area versus Length

1. Look at the prebuilt cubes. For each, measure the length of each side of the cube.

2. Also, determine the surface area of one face of the cube. Record your data in a data table.

Length of cube (cm)	Surface area of face (cm²)

Equipment

Four graduated cylinders marked for each liquid, four beakers containing different liquids, paper towels (to clean spills), digital scale, four plastic pipettes marked for each liquid, a printed list that has the density of each of the four liquids used.

Assembly

It is important to have four liquids with different densities. Suggested liquids include: isopropyl alcohol (0.785 g/cm³); milk (about 1.4 g/cm³); olive oil (about 0.850 g/cm³); water (1 g/cm³); vegetable oil (0.92 g/cm³); honey (1.4 g/cm³)].

It is important that the students zero the scale after placing the 100 mL graduated cylinder on it.

Station 3: Liquids: Volume versus Density

1. At this station, use a graduated cylinder to measure the volume of a 50.0 g sample of each liquid.

2. Make sure that the cylinders are clean and dry before you begin.

3. Place a graduated cylinder on the scale and zero the scale.

4. Carefully, using the pipette, add liquid to the graduated cylinder until the scale reads 50.0 g.

5. Use the markings on the graduated cylinder to determine the volume of the liquid inside the cylinder.

6. Record the given density and volume for this liquid in the data table.

7. Pour the liquid from the graduated cylinder back into its original container.

8. Repeat steps 2–7 for each of the liquids.

Liquid number	Density (g/cm³)	Volume of 50.0 g (mL)
1		
2		
3		
4		

Analysis and Conclusions

Station 1

1. Produce a graph of mass versus number of washers for both types of washers on the same graph. Use a different color for the small and larger washers.

2. Draw the best fit curve or line for each set of data.

3. Compare and contrast your graphs. How are they similar? How are they different?

The graphs are both straight lines and have the same y-intercept. The large washer

line has a larger slope.

4. Do your lines or curves go through the origin? Why or why not?

No. They do not because the mass includes the mass of the container.

5. Does the y-intercept for these graphs tell you anything about the experimental design of this station?

It tells me that the mass of the container is about 15 g.

6. What does the slope of the graphs tell you about the experimental design?

The slope of the line is the mass of the washers. Because the larger washers have

more mass, they have a larger slope.

7. Using the form $y = mx + b$, write an equation for each line.

Answers will vary. Total mass = (mass of single washer) (number of washers) + mass

of container.

8. How would the graph be different if we used even larger washers and no container?

Larger washers would mean a steeper slope. No container would mean that the line

would have a y-intercept of 0.

Station 2

1. Produce a graph of the area of the face versus the length of the side of the cube.
2. Draw your best fit line or curve for this graph.
3. Does this graph go through the origin? Why or why not?

Yes. It makes sense that a cube with side length 0 would have surface area of 0.

4. Predict the surface area if the cube's side length was 5 cm.

Answers will vary.

Station 3

1. Produce a graph of volume versus density.

2. What type of relationship exists between volume and density?

   The shape of the graph indicates that this is an inverse relationship.

3. Imagine you are given another liquid that has a density of 2 g/cm³. Using your graph, predict the volume of this liquid that masses 50 g.

   Answers will vary.

Chapter 1 Lab Missing Identity

Your Task

You will be given an object made from an unknown material. Your task is to develop an experimental procedure that allows the unknown material to be identified and that can be followed by anyone.

Equipment Provided

- ruler
- digital scale
- stopwatch
- chart
- spring scale
- graduated cylinder

Requirements

- You must design an experiment to solve the problem.
- Your procedure should be thorough enough that another student in the class could follow your instructions.
- Present your data in tables, if possible.
- Show calculations used to solve the problem, if applicable.
- List at least two sources of error. For each, indicate what effect the error would have on your results.

Materials Provided

Unknown object

Procedure Followed

List your procedure as a set of steps that another student in the class could easily follow.

Check experimental design for safety considerations before allowing the

students to proceed.

_____

_____

_____

_____

_____

_____

_____

_____

Time to Set Up: <1 h
Time in Lab: 1 h
Performance Assessment

This lab assessment will test students' ability to develop an experimental design, take accurate data, and represent that data appropriately. Students will most likely decide to use density to complete this task. You should have charts with the densities of various materials available. Because this is the first time students are performing this type of assessment, they may need more assistance.

Equipment
In addition to the ones listed, you will need to find objects to give the students. Density sets are available from science stores. You can also use everyday items, but be aware that some students may not know about using water displacement to find volume. Each group should have a different object. Preferably, the objects should be made from different materials.

Data Collected

Record all your data in appropriate charts in the space below.

Emphasize the importance of representing data in charts or graphs.

Make certain that the charts and graphs contain the correct units for the

quantities measured.

_____

_____

_____

_____

Conclusion

Identify your material. Use your data to support your answer.

_____

_____

_____

_____

_____

Sources of Error

Possible sources of error include:

• Error in measuring the mass (accuracy of scale, item wet from water

  displacement determination)

• Error in measuring the volume (water splashed during water displacement,

  accuracy of ruler)

_____

_____

_____

_____

Chapter 2 Lab   Describing Motion with Position versus Time Graphs

Purpose

In this lab, you will use a motion detector to produce graphs of different types of motion. You will then analyze each graph produced and relate it to the type of motion used to produce it.

Materials

- motion detector
- computer or handheld interface
- masking tape
- sheet of cardboard
- meter stick

Discussion

The motion detector is a device for measuring the position of an object relative to the detector. The motion detector sends out a series of high-frequency pulses of sound. These pulses reflect from an object in their path and return to a detector. Computer software measures the time elapsed between the sending of the original pulse and the detection of the reflected pulse. The computer uses this time, along with the speed of sound in air, to determine the position.

Time to Set Up: <1 h
Time in Lab: 1 h
Qualitative Lab

Motion detectors are available from several vendors. It is important that you have the correct hardware for the detectors. The motion detector measures how far the object is from the detector. As a result, moving away from the detector will show a positive displacement and velocity. Using whiteboards or pieces of cardboard as reflectors can produce better data.

Check the motion detectors before the students arrive to be certain they are functioning properly.

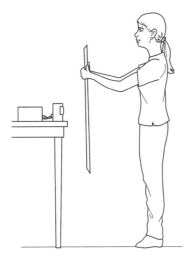

Procedure

1. Position the motion detector on the edge of the table so it is aimed horizontally and is about chest high.

2. Use short strips of masking tape to mark off a 4-m-long path on the floor in front of the detector. Place the strips at half-meter intervals.

3. Turn on the computer and open the motion-detecting software.

4. Select the software option that graphs position versus time.

5. Decide which group members will make movements and which will operate the computer.

6. Use the motion detector to produce position versus time graphs of the motions described below. Either sketch the graphs shown on the computer screen on a separate sheet of paper or print them out.

Trial 1. A person stands at the 2 m mark and remains there.

Trial 2. A person stands at the 2 m mark and sways gently side to side.

Trial 3. A person walks slowly away from the detector, beginning at the 0.5 m mark.

Trial 4. A person walks quickly away from the detector, beginning at the 0.5 m mark.

Trial 5. A person walks slowly toward the detector, beginning at the 4 m mark.

Trial 6. A person walks quickly toward the detector, beginning at the 4 m mark.

Trial 7. A person walks slowly away from the detector beginning at the 0.5 m mark, stops for a few seconds, and then returns to the 0.5 m mark.

Students should move very slightly to the right and left. The motion detector does not register motion in this plane and should show a constant 2 m displacement. If students move too much, the motion detector may "see" the back wall.

Analysis and Conclusions

1. Which of the trials (1 through 7) produced horizontal lines on the position versus time graph?

Trials 1, 2, and 7 should all have a horizontal line. Trials 1 and 2 should be horizontal for the entire trial, while trial 7 should be horizontal only while the person was stopped.

Based on your answer, what kind of motion produces a horizontal line on a position versus time graph?

A position versus time graph is horizontal when an object is at rest or moving only perpendicular to the direction of the motion detector's pulses.

2. Describe the difference between the graphs produced in trials 3 and 4.

The graphs look similar except for their slopes. Trial 4 had a steeper slope than trial 3.

3. Describe the difference between the graphs produced in trials 3 and 5.

   The two graphs start at different points. Trial 3 has a small positive slope and trial 5

   has a small negative slope.

4. What effect did moving side to side (trial 2) have on the position versus time graph?

   This has no effect on the graph at all.

5. What does the slope of the position versus time graph represent?

   The slope of the position versus time graph represents the velocity of the object.

6. How would you move in order to produce a position versus time graph that initially has a large positive slope followed by a smaller negative slope?

   Start close to the detector and move away quickly, then reverse and move slowly

   back toward the detector.

Chapter 2 Lab   Skip, Run, Walk, Rest

Purpose

In this lab, you will gain a better understanding of the meaning of the shape of a position versus time graph.

Discussion

Position versus time graphs not only tell where an object is located at a specific time, but can also be used to determine the motion of the object. In today's lab, you will perform tasks and produce a position versus time graph for these tasks. After this lab, you should be able to predict the shape of a position versus time graph for a given motion.

Required Equipment/Supplies

• tape measure
• chalk
• stopwatches

Procedure ⚠

1. Use the chalk to mark a starting line.

2. Measure in a straight line and make marks at 5, 10, and 15 m from the starting line.

3. Choose one team member to be the "runner." It is important that the runner maintain a constant velocity during each phase of the trial.

4. Choose three team members to be timers. There should be one timer at each of the 5 m, 10 m, and 15 m marks. They start timing when the runner begins and stop when the runner passes their mark.

5. The "runner" runs, walks, rests (for 10 seconds), and skips at a constant velocity between the marks made in step 2. The runner can choose these "motions" in any order, but must cycle through all four of them.

6. The runner begins at the starting point.

7. When signaled, the runner begins to cycle through the motions, each time progressing 5 m farther from the starting line (except when resting).

8. Students should record the change in position, time, and motion for each segment of the run.

9. When all four motions are complete, students should switch roles and repeat the lab.

Time to Set Up: 1 h
Time in Lab: 1 h
Quantitative Lab

This lab is best performed outside. Sidewalks with chalk marks work well. If weather or facilities do not allow working outside, the lab is easily done in the hallway.

Students will use +5 m or 0 m as the change in position for each interval. They should record the total time from the beginning to the end of the interval.

Data

Runner: _____	Initial position: _____	
Change in position (m)	Time (s)	Motion

Runner: _____	Initial position: _____	
Change in position (m)	Time (s)	Motion

Analysis and Conclusions

1. Draw the position versus time graph for both runners on the same piece of graph paper. Use a different color for each runner.

2. Why can we use straight lines on our position versus time graphs for this lab?
   We assume that the runner uses a constant velocity during each phase of the graph.
   _____

3. Which runner had the largest average skipping speed?
   Students' answers will vary. _____

4. Without doing any calculations, do you think the runners ever had the same speed (not necessarily at the same time)? If so, when?
   Students should look for similar slopes. If the slopes seem similar, then they might
   think the runners had the same speed. _____

   What makes you think so?
   _____
   _____

5. Determine the average velocity for all motions and fill in the chart. What method did you use?

Students' answers will vary. Students might find the slope of each line on their graphs

or take the displacement for each interval divided by the time for that interval.

Runner: _____	
Motion (Run, skip, rest, or walk)	**Average velocity (m/s)**
Motion 1:	
Motion 2:	
Motion 3:	
Motion 4:	
Average velocity for entire trial:	

Runner: _____	
Motion (Run, skip, rest, or walk)	**Average velocity (m/s)**
Motion 1:	
Motion 2:	
Motion 3:	
Motion 4:	
Average velocity for entire trial:	

6. Produce a velocity versus time graph for both runners on the same graph.

7. Consider the following hypothetical lab data for two runners who start at the same time.

Runner #1 Initial position: 0 m		
Motion	**Change in position (m)**	**Time (s)**
Run	+5	1.5
Skip	+5	3.9
Walk	−5	6.9
Rest	0	16.9

Runner #2 Initial position: 10 m		
Motion	Position (m)	Times (s)
Rest	0	10
Skip	−5	12.3
Run	+5	14.5
Walk	−5	17.5

a. Produce a position versus time graph for both runners on the same graph.

b. Do the runners ever have the same velocity at the same time? How can you tell?

Yes, they are both at rest between 6.9 and 10 seconds. The graphs have the same

slope.

c. At what time(s) are the runners at the same place at the same time?

At 3.9 seconds and 12.3 seconds

d. Which is the faster runner?

Runner 1 is faster.

Chapter 2: Introduction to Motion • **Performance Task**

Chapter 2 Lab   SMASH!

Your Task

You will be given a constant-velocity car. Your task is to work together with another group to predict where and when your cars will collide.

Equipment Provided

- constant-velocity car
- meter stick
- tape measure
- digital scale
- stopwatch

Requirements

- You must design an experiment to solve the problem.
- You will receive one car to experiment with before the actual trial.
- You will rely on your "sister" group to provide data from their car.
- Your instructor will provide the exact locations for the starting point for each car.
- You will turn in your time/location predictions to your instructor before the cars are released.
- Show calculations/graphs used to solve the problem, if applicable.
- List at least two sources of error. For each, indicate what effect the error would have on your results.

Procedure Followed

List your procedure as a set of steps that another student in the class could easily follow.

Students may choose to solve the problem using a system of equations by

substituting the values for both cars into $x = vt + x_0$.

_____

_____

Another method involves graphing the two cars' motions on a single position

versus time graph and finding the intersection point of the two graphs.

_____

_____

_____

_____

_____

Time to Set Up: <1 h
Time in Lab: 1 h
Performance Assessment

Students will work first in small groups (e.g., A–F). Each small group will receive a car. After finding the speed of their cars, two of these small groups (e.g., A and C) come together and share data. You then provide them with a starting location and direction for each car. For example, car A will start at 5 m and travel up the tape measure while car C starts at 10 m and travels down. Students must provide their predicted collision location and time before starting the cars.

Assembly

You will need one car per group. The cars should have different speeds. This can be accomplished by using new or used batteries, or by replacing one battery with a cylinder of aluminum foil. Place a tape measure on the floor in a long hallway and tape it to the floor.

Data Collected

This includes data provided by another group. Record all your data in appropriate charts in the space below.

_____

_____

_____

_____

_____

_____

_____

_____

_____

Conclusion

Predict the time and location of the collision. Use data to support your answer.

_____

_____

_____

_____

_____

Sources of Error

Possible sources of error include:

• The cars don't always travel straight.

• Batteries wear out, causing cars to slow down.

• Difficulty measuring time or length.

• Placement of cars on the tape measure.

• Difficulty of releasing the cars at exactly the same time.

Chapter 3: Acceleration and Accelerated Motion • *v* vs. *t* graphs

Chapter 3 Lab   Think Slope

Purpose

In Experiment 1 of this lab, you will predict and sketch graphs of position, velocity, and acceleration, all as a function of time, for a variety of motions. You will then use a motion detector to check your predictions. In Experiment 2, you will analyze graphs to produce a written description of the motion and then test your predictions using the motion detector.

Materials

- motion detector
- computer or lab interface
- masking tape
- sheet of cardboard
- meter stick

Discussion

Kinematics is the branch of physics concerned with describing how things move. In particular, kinematics examines the relationships between position, velocity, and acceleration. While these quantities, and the connections between them, may be expressed with equations, graphs provide an equally powerful and sometimes more direct method of describing motion.

A great deal can be learned about the motion of an object just by looking at graphs of its position, velocity, or acceleration versus time. In this lab, you will learn that, given a graph of any of these three quantities, it is possible, at least in principle, to determine the nature of the other two.

Procedure

Setup

1. Position the motion detector on the edge of the table so it is aimed horizontally and is about chest high.

2. Use short strips of masking tape to mark off a 4-m-long path on the floor in front of the detector. Place the strips at 0.5 m intervals.

3. Turn on the computer and open motion-detecting software.

4. Select the software option that graphs position, velocity, and acceleration versus time simultaneously.

5. Walk back and forth in front of the detector to determine if all three graphs are responding and providing a reasonable representation of your motion.

In this lab, students use a motion detector to produce graphs of position, velocity, and acceleration versus time. They will also learn the significance of the slopes of these graphs, and how the graphs relate to one another.

Time to Set Up: <1 h
Time in Lab: 1 h
Inquiry Lab

Most motion detectors do not detect objects closer than 0.5 m or farther away than 5 m. Also, the detector emits sound in a 30° cone; anything within that cone can cause a reflection. Calculations of velocity and acceleration done by the computer are extremely sensitive to small variations in motion, so instruct students to move as smoothly as possible.

Test the motion detector and computer setups prior to class. Give each group of students a sheet of cardboard that is 8 1/2" × 11" or larger. This will help motion detectors track students' movements more reliably.

Experiment 1

1. In the space provided, sketch the position, velocity, and acceleration graphs corresponding to each of the following four motions:

   a. Have a person (starting at the detector) walk quickly away from the detector at a constant speed and then slowly come to a stop.

   b. Have a person (starting near the far end of the detector's range) walk slowly at a constant rate toward the detector and then slowly come to a stop.

   c. Have a person (starting near the detector) rapidly increase their speed at a constant rate while walking away from the detector and then slowly come to a stop.

   d. Have a person (starting near the far end of the detector's range) rapidly increase their speed at a constant rate while walking toward the detector and then slowly come to a stop.

2. Check the graphs you created by using the motion detector to produce graphs of the prescribed motions.

Experiment 2

For the graphs below, write a description of each motion in the space provided. Use the motion detector to test your description. (*Note:* When needed, initial positions and velocities are given.)

a.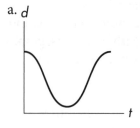

A. The person starts from rest near the far end of the detector's range and, after experiencing a negative acceleration, moves with a constant negative velocity. After stopping for an instant, the person experiences a positive acceleration, followed by a positive constant velocity. The motion concludes with a period of negative acceleration, which brings the person to rest.

_____

_____

b. The velocity versus time graph for a person with an initial position near the detector is shown below.

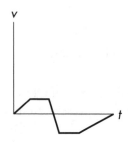

The person starts near the detector, experiences a constant positive acceleration, followed by a constant positive velocity. After slowing down and stopping briefly, the person accelerates toward the motion detector and then travels with a constant negative velocity.

The motion concludes with a positive acceleration, which brings the

person to rest.

_____

_____

c. The acceleration versus time graph for a person initially at rest (zero velocity) near the detector is shown below.

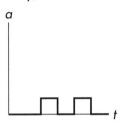

The person is standing still for a while

and then experiences a constant positive

acceleration. The positive acceleration is

followed by a period of constant positive

velocity (zero acceleration). The person's

motion finishes with positive acceleration.

_____

_____

_____

_____

Data

Experiment 1

a. *d* versus *t*   *v* versus *t*   *a* versus *t*

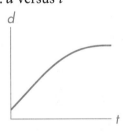   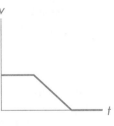   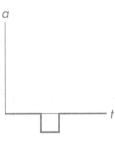

(a)

b. *d* versus *t*   *v* versus *t*   *a* versus *t*

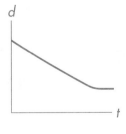   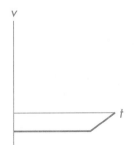   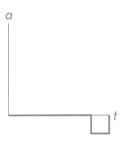

(b)

c. *d* versus *t*   *v* versus *t*   *a* versus *t*

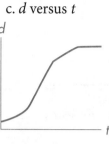
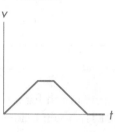

(c)

d. *d* versus *t*   *v* versus *t*   *a* versus *t*

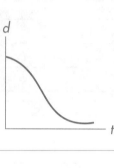
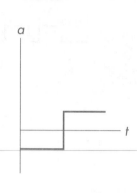

(d)

Analysis and Conclusions

1. What does the slope of the position versus time graph indicate?

   The slope of the position versus time graph equals the velocity. _____

   _____

2. What does the slope of the velocity versus time graph indicate?

   The slope of the velocity versus time graph equals the acceleration. _____

   _____

3. How can you tell from a position versus time graph that an object has changed direction?

   The slope of the curve changes sign. _____

   _____

4. What does the amount of curvature of the line on a position versus time graph indicate?

   The amount of curvature represents the magnitude of the acceleration. _____

   _____

5. Is it possible to tell from the acceleration versus time graph that an object has changed direction? Explain.

No. The acceleration versus time graph conveys how the velocity is changing with

time. Because it does not contain information about the object's initial velocity, there

is no way of telling if the object has changed direction.

6. What is the sign of the acceleration if the position versus time graph has an (a) upward curvature; (b) downward curvature?

An upward curvature indicates a positive acceleration. A downward curvature

indicates a negative acceleration.

7. In which of the trials were there a positive velocity and a negative acceleration during at least a portion of the motion?

Trials a and c represented motions with a positive velocity and a negative

acceleration.

8. Is an object necessarily slowing down if it is experiencing a negative acceleration? Explain.

No, it is not necessarily slowing down. It will be slowing down if the velocity is

positive and the acceleration is negative. However, it will be speeding up if both the

velocity and the acceleration are negative.

9. Describe the shape of the position, velocity, and acceleration graphs as a person speeds up away from the detector at a constant acceleration.

The position versus time graph has an increasing positive slope (i.e., curved upward),

the velocity versus time graph has a constant positive slope, and the line on the

acceleration versus time graph has a positive value with zero slope.

10. In Experiment 1, compare your sketched velocity graphs for part a and part b with the actual velocity graphs produced by the motion detector. At the start, the sketch and predicted graphs should be different. Explain why this is so.

The runner had to accelerate to the constant speed in each case. A region of

acceleration should be present at the start of each graph.

Chapter 3: Acceleration and Accelerated Motion • Acceleration

Chapter 3 Lab   The Shuttle Run

Purpose

In this lab, you will simulate a shuttle run and will develop a better understanding of what it means to accelerate.

Materials

- pen or pencil
- graph paper

Discussion

Imagine you are back in gym class. The teacher has two lines drawn at the sides of the gym. You must start at one line, run to the other, stop and touch it, and then run back and stop on the first line. The goal is to do this as quickly as possible without overshooting either line. This activity is a simulation of running the shuttle run. Good luck!

Procedure ⚠

1. Two people can race on the same track if each uses a different color pen or pencil. Both players should choose a spot on the starting line and then take turns moving as described below.

2. You must follow these rules as you play the game.

   a. Start by moving a single square.

   b. On the next move, maintain the same velocity or change the velocity by +/− 1 square. For example, in your next move, you could maintain your velocity and go another 1 square to the right. You could speed up and go 2 spaces to the right or slow down and not move.

   c. Do not cross the lines at the extremes of the course. You must stop on the lines AND obey the movement rules outlined in part b.

   d. Make dots on the graph to show your progression; number them.

   e. The person who completes the run in the fewest number of steps wins.

The goal of this simulated shuttle run is to give students a conceptual understanding of acceleration. In particular, they will learn that acceleration is a general term meaning any change in velocity, not just speeding up. Students may get competitive and want to do several trials, so it's a good idea to have extra graph paper available.

Time to Set Up: <1 h
Time in Lab <1 h
Quantitative Lab

This is a sample of a completed shuttle run. Note that the moves are numbered.

3. It may take several attempts to complete the task without passing the lines at the extremes. Once you have a successful trip, use these steps to fill in the chart in the analysis section.

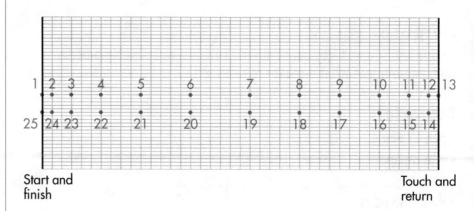

Start and finish

Touch and return

Students will have 20+ steps and will need to complete these charts on a separate sheet of paper.

Analysis and Conclusions

1. For these charts, assume that each square is 0.5 m in length and each move required 0.25 second. On a separate sheet of paper, copy the chart formats below and complete for the entire run.

Step	Change in position (Δx)	Velocity (m/s)
0		
1		
2		

Between steps	Change in velocity (m/s)	Acceleration (m/s²)
0 and 1		
1 and 2		
2 and 3		

2. When you first attempted to do the shuttle run, you probably went past the end lines. Use the terms acceleration and velocity to explain what you did wrong.

Usually, students accelerate to a very large velocity and lack the time necessary to slow down and stop on the left-hand end line.

3. Describe the motion of the runner when the velocity and acceleration were both positive.

The runner was moving to the right and speeding up.

4. Describe the motion of the runner when the velocity was positive and the acceleration negative.

The runner was moving to the right and slowing down.

5. Describe the motion of the runner when the velocity was negative and the acceleration positive.

The runner was moving to the left and slowing down.

6. Describe the motion of the runner when both the velocity and the acceleration were negative.

The runner was moving to the left and speeding up.

7. Based on your answers above, make a generalization about the motion of the runner and the signs of the velocity and acceleration.

The sign of the velocity determines the direction the runner is traveling.

If the acceleration has the same sign, then the runner is speeding up.

If the acceleration and velocity have different signs, then the runner is

slowing down.

8. Make graphs of position versus time, velocity versus time, and acceleration versus time for a successful trial.

    a. Position versus time

    These are sample graphs. Students' graphs will vary.

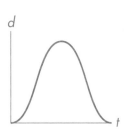

b. Velocity versus time

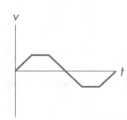

c. Acceleration versus time

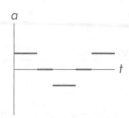

9. Describe the shape of the position versus time and velocity versus time graphs when the runner had a positive acceleration.

When the runner has a positive acceleration, the position graph is
curved upward like a smile. The velocity graph is a straight line with a
positive slope.

10. Describe the shape of the position versus time and velocity versus time graphs when the runner had a negative acceleration.

When the runner has a negative acceleration, the position graph has a
downward curve like a frown, and the velocity graph is a straight line
with a negative slope.

Chapter 3: Acceleration and Accelerated Motion • **Performance Task**

Chapter 3 Lab   Sprinter

Your Task

One member of your group will start from rest and accelerate until he or she reaches a constant speed. You must determine the average acceleration of the runner and his or her final velocity.

Equipment Provided

- tape measure
- stopwatch

Requirements

- You must design an experiment to solve the problem.
- You may request additional equipment from your instructor.
- Your instructor must approve your method BEFORE you begin experimenting.
- Show calculations/graphs used to solve the problem, if applicable.
- List at least two sources of error. For each, indicate what effect the error would have on your results.

Procedure Followed ⚠

List your procedure as a set of steps that another student in the class could easily follow.

Students might choose to make marks every 5 m for a length of 25 m. They would then determine how long it takes the runner to reach each mark. They could produce a position versus time graph and generate the velocity and acceleration versus time graphs. Computer graphing software would make this process fairly easy. If you don't want your students to use the graphing programs, you should indicate that at the beginning of the lab. Students may choose to use a motion detector. The range on most detectors is less than 5 m. Allow the students to try this method. It may not give them the results they hope for, however. Students could also video record the runner and use video analysis to determine the position of the runner at given time intervals. Graphing these data, they could produce the motion graphs for the runner.

Students' approaches to this task can vary from very low-tech (stopwatches) to very high-tech (video recording the runner and using frame-by-frame analysis). Encourage them to think "outside the box." If time is available, the lab could be followed by students' presentations of their methods.

Time to Set Up: <1 h
Time in Lab: 1 h
Performance Assessment

Check the procedure for safety. Remind the students that safety is a priority and they don't need to sprint so fast that they fall.

Equipment Requested

Students bring their experimental design complete with an equipment list for your approval before doing any experimentation. They might request items such as a video camera, motion detector, chalk, or multiple stopwatches. It is helpful to have these items easily accessible but out of sight.

Data Collected

Record all your data in appropriate charts in the space below. Include any graphs in this space, as well.

Conclusion

Use your data/graphs to determine the average acceleration and the final velocity of your runner.

_____

_____

_____

_____

_____

Sources of Error

List two sources of error and what effect they have on your results.
Possible sources of error include:

• Difficulty measuring the exact time the runner crosses a marking.

• The runner might accelerate for only a short time, and thus the average acceleration will depend on how much of the constant-velocity phase is included in the trial.

• If students do multiple trials, the acceleration and velocity will vary and probably decrease as the runner tires.

Chapter 3: Acceleration and Accelerated Motion • Acceleration Due to Gravity and the Effects of Air Resistance

Chapter 3 Lab   Free Fall Exploration

Time to Set Up: >1 h
Time in Lab: 1 h
Qualitative Lab

Purpose

In this lab, you will examine how objects fall under the influence of gravity with and without the opposing force of air resistance.

Materials

Necessary materials will be found at each station.

Discussion

In everyday life, different objects often appear to fall at different rates. Autumn leaves slowly drift to earth, whereas an acorn may drop like a rock. Observations such as these seem to indicate that heavier objects fall faster than lighter ones. Is this actually the case, or are there other factors affecting how objects fall?

When you have completed this lab, you will have an understanding of how gravity and air resistance determine how objects fall.

Procedure

Station 1: Falling Objects

Hold a book horizontally above the floor at the same height as a rubber stopper. Release the two objects simultaneously. Drop the book so that it lands flat on its cover, not on a corner. Compare the time required for the objects to reach the floor. Drop the objects several times to confirm your observations. What does this tell you about the rate at which objects of different mass fall?

The book and stopper should be observed to reach the floor at the same

time. This suggests that all objects, regardless of mass, accelerate at the

same rate when acted on solely by gravity. The effects of air resistance are

assumed to be negligible because the ratio of mass to surface area is quite

large for both objects.

Equipment
Book, rubber stopper

Use an old book that is no longer needed for classroom use.

Station 2: Falling Objects and Air Resistance

Simultaneously drop a sheet of paper and a stopper from the same height. Which object reaches the floor first? Now crumple the paper into a tight ball. Drop the crumpled paper and rubber stopper from the

Equipment
Sheet of notebook paper, rubber stopper

same height, once again releasing them at the same time. What do you observe? Compare the results obtained with the crumpled and the flat sheet of paper. How do you account for these results?

The upward force due to air resistance acting on the open sheet of paper

opposes the downward force of gravity. This results in a lower rate of descent.

Because of the stopper's small surface area, it falls virtually unimpeded by the

air. Wadding the paper up into a ball greatly reduces its surface area, which in

turn reduces the air resistance encountered by the paper.

Station 3: The Effect of Free Fall on Friction

Equipment
Two disk magnets, wooden pencil

The disk magnets should have holes in their centers. Such magnets are sometimes referred to as "donut" magnets. Magnets with diameters ranging from 3 to 6 cm work well.

On a horizontally held wooden pencil, place two disk magnets with opposite poles facing each other. The magnets should be situated so that they are just beyond the point where they move toward each other due to magnetic attraction. Release the pencil and observe the magnets as the pencil/ magnet assembly falls. What do you observe? Why do you think this occurs?

The magnets should not move while the pencil is being held. When the

pencil is released, the magnets will come together. When the pencil/magnet

assembly is stationary, the force of friction keeps the magnets from moving

toward each other. When the assembly is released, the pencil and magnets

fall with the same acceleration. This eliminates the normal force and

therefore the frictional force between the pencil and magnets.

Station 4: The Effect of Free Fall on Pressure

Equipment
Cup, water, catch basin, pail, towels

Assembly
Use a nail to punch a hole in the side of a plastic cup near its bottom. Place the pail full of water on the table and the catch basin on the floor.

Hold your thumb over the hole as you fill the cup with water. Holding the cup as high as possible, remove your thumb and let the water stream out into a catch basin on the floor. Now drop the cup into the catch basin. Clean up any spilled water. What causes the water to squirt out of the cup before it is released? Describe what happens while the cup is falling. Explain your observation.

When the water-filled cup is being held, the liquid is pulled down by the

force of gravity. This causes pressure on the water at the opening in the

side of the cup. It is this pressure that forces water out the hole. While

the cup is falling, the cup and water fall at the same rate, eliminating this

pressure at the opening. Thus, the water stops squirting out of the hole

while the cup is falling.

Station 5: *Fall* in Free Fall Does Not Mean an Object Is Necessarily Moving Downward

Invert the groan tube. Notice that the whistle inside the tube produces a groaning sound as it falls through the tube. Now invert the tube again.

With the whistle sounding, immediately toss the tube straight up into the air. Describe the sound before, during, and after the tube is launched. Explain your observations.

When the groan tube is turned upside down, a whistle falls through the tube. Air passing through the falling whistle produces a groaning sound. If the tube is thrown upward while the whistle is falling, the groaning will stop and will not resume until the groan tube is caught. This occurs because, while airborne, both the tube and the whistle are being acted on solely by the force of gravity and therefore experience the same acceleration. Because both are accelerating at the same rate, there is no relative motion between the tube and the whistle, and the groaning stops.

Station 6: The Weight of an Object in Free Fall

Attach a 500 g mass to a spring scale. Observe the reading on the scale. Lift the mass and scale approximately a meter above a pillow or cushion. Watch the reading on the scale as the mass and scale fall together. What does the scale read as the two objects fall? Explain your observation.

After the scale is released, both the mass and the scale are in free fall. Because the two objects are accelerating at the same rate, the scale no longer supports the mass. With the spring in the scale no longer stretched, the scale reads zero.

Station 7: Free Fall Is Symmetric

Toss a ball straight up into the air. When the ball reaches its maximum height, have your lab partner drop a second ball from this same height. Observe the motion of the two balls as they fall. What effect did the tossed ball's ascent have on its downward motion? Explain your answer.

The tossed ball's ascent has no effect on its downward motion. The tossed ball's velocity is zero when it reaches its maximum height, as is the velocity of the dropped ball. Because both balls descend from the same height with the same initial speed and acceleration, they will stay together as they fall.

Station 8: The Effect of Height on Final Velocity

Stand on a chair holding the string with equally spaced washers above the pie pan. Make sure the string is fully extended vertically and the pan is on the floor. Release the string and listen carefully.

Stand on a chair holding the string with unequally spaced washers above the pie pan. Make sure the string is fully extended vertically and the pan is on the floor. Release the string and listen carefully.

Equipment
Groan tube

The groan tube is a toy that consists of a whistle contained within a plastic tube. The device makes a distinct groaning sound when turned on end. The toy is inexpensive and available from a variety of toy distributors.

Equipment
500 g mass, spring scale, pillow or cushion

Observation time is very short, so students must be prepared to read the scale as it falls. Using a scale with a large face is helpful. To prevent damage to the scale and floor, it is important that a soft object be used to cushion the fall of the mass and scale.

Equipment
Two rubber balls

Practice may be required to coordinate the dropping of the second ball just as the first ball reaches its maximum height.

Equipment
Two 2 m lengths of string, twelve washers, two aluminum pie pans

Assembly

String #1: Starting from one end of the string, tie washers onto the string so they are spaced 30 cm apart. Tape the end of the string to a pie pan so that the first washer is 30 cm from the pan.

String #2: Starting from one end, tie washers onto the string with the following distances between them: 5 cm, 15 cm, 25 cm, 35 cm, 45 cm, and 55 cm. The last washer should be 180 cm from the end. Tape the end to a pie pan so that the first washer is 5 cm from the pan.

[Free Fall #1]
```
A-------x--------x-------
x-------x--------x------B
C-x--x----x--------x-----
------x----------------D
```

Compare the rhythm of the sounds produced by each collection of washers. How do you explain your observations?

Students should observe that the evenly spaced washers produce tapping sounds at an ever-increasing rate, whereas the unevenly spaced washers make sounds at even intervals. Washers that start farther from the floor end up falling faster. The uneven spacing of washers compensates for this by putting increasing distances between washers that fall with higher speeds.

Chapter 3: Acceleration and Accelerated Motion • Acceleration due to Gravity

Chapter 3 Lab   Finding "g" . . . Three Ways

Purpose

In this lab, you will use three different methods to determine the value of the acceleration due to gravity on earth.

Materials

- motion detector
- computer or handheld interface
- tennis ball
- tape measure
- stopwatch
- picket fence
- photogate timer
- ringstand and clamps

Discussion

When an object is in free fall (and we neglect air resistance), the only force acting on it is the gravitational attraction between the object and the earth. This means that the object is experiencing an external net force and thus must accelerate in the direction of this force. You will determine the magnitude of this acceleration using three different methods. Take note of the difficulties and assumptions made in each method, as you will be asked to evaluate the methods for their accuracy.

Procedure—Method 1: Ball Drop

Equipment

- ball
- tape measure
- stopwatch

1. Find a stairwell or similar place where you can drop the ball from as large a height as possible.
2. Measure the height the ball will drop and record this in your data table.
3. Drop the ball from this height five times. For each drop, measure the time it takes the ball to fall and enter these values in the data table.

In this lab, students use three different methods to determine the value of *g*: the kinematics equations, the motion detector, and a device called a picket fence. (The picket fence is a striped piece of plastic which, when dropped through a photogate timer, allows the computer to produce a velocity versus time graph.)

Time to Set Up: 1 h
Time in Lab: 1 h
Quantitative Lab

There are three different labs for the students to complete. It may be best to set up two of each lab and have the students rotate through them.

A stairwell works best.

It may be helpful to have the motion detector set up before the students come to class. C clamps work well to attach the ringstand to the table.

Procedure—Method 2: Motion Detector

Equipment
- ball
- motion detector
- clamps
- ringstand
- computer or handheld interface

1. Place the ringstand on a table and use a clamp to secure it to the table. Use a second clamp to attach the motion detector to the top of the stand so that it faces the floor. Make sure the motion detector extends beyond the edge of the table.

2. With the motion detector connected to the computer or handheld interface, open the correct file to display motion graphs.

3. Hold the ball about 20 cm from the motion detector. Start the motion detector and drop the ball. Make sure your hand is not blocking the motion detector's "view" of the falling ball.

4. Repeat this a few times until you think you have a good trial.

5. Sketch the position, velocity, and acceleration versus time graphs below.

6. Using the software on the computer or handheld device, determine the acceleration of the ball. Write your answer in the data section below.

Procedure—Method 3: Picket Fence

Equipment
- picket fence
- computer or handheld interface
- photogate timer
- ringstand
- clamps
- cushion

The picket fence might break if it hits the floor or table. Check the software that comes with your photogate timer to locate the correct file for the students to use.

1. Place the ringstand on a table and use a clamp to secure it to the table. Use a second clamp to attach the photogate timer to the stand so that the picket fence can fall through the timer.

2. Activate the photogate and drop the picket fence through it and onto the cushion. Try to drop the picket fence so that it travels straight down.

3. The computer will display the graphs of velocity versus time.

4. Use the software to determine the slope of the velocity versus time graph. Record this value in the data table.

5. Repeat steps 2–4 two more times and record these data.

Data and Analysis

Method 1
Height of drop _____ m

Trial	Time (s)

1. When the ball is dropped, what is its initial velocity?
   The initial velocity was 0.

2. Determine the average time for the ball to drop for all five trials.
   Students' answers will vary.

3. Using the average time and starting velocity, calculate the
   acceleration of the ball.
   Students should use the equation $x = 0.5\ at^2$.

Method 2
d versus t v versus t a versus t

Measured acceleration _____ m/s^2

Method 3

Trial	Slope (m/s^2)
1	
2	
3	

Conclusions

1. What does the slope of the *v* versus *t* graph tell you about the motion of the picket fence?

2. In the chart below, record the average values of "*g*" that you found using each of the methods.

	Acceleration due to gravity (m/s^2)
1	
2	
3	

% error = {(Accepted − Experimental)/Accepted} × 100%

3. The accepted value for "*g*" is approximately 9.81 m/s^2. Determine the percent error for each of the methods used.

Method	% error
1	
2	
3	

4. Which method resulted in the least percent error? Explain why this method was the most accurate.

   Students' answers will vary. The methods that used the computer should be the most accurate.

5. Which method was least accurate? What errors existed in this method that did not exist in the best method?

   Students' answers will vary. The first method contains the most error because the reaction time of the people doing the timing adds to the error.

Chapter 3: Acceleration and Accelerated Motion • Performance Task

Chapter 3 Lab   Launch Speed, Please

Your Task

You will be given a device capable of launching an object straight upward. You must determine the launch velocity of the object. You will design and perform an experiment to accomplish this task.

Equipment Provided

- launcher
- object

Safety 🔒

All students must wear protective goggles during experimentation.

Requirements

- You must design an experiment to solve the problem.
- You may request additional equipment from your instructor.
- Your instructor must approve your method BEFORE you begin experimenting.
- Show calculations/graphs used to solve the problem, if applicable.
- List at least two sources of error. For each, indicate the effect the error would have on your results.

Equipment Requested

Students will most likely ask for stopwatches. Some might ask for meter sticks or motion detectors, as well. Have these items readily available but out of sight of the students.

Procedure Followed

List your procedure as a set of steps that another student in the class could easily follow.

The easiest method is to time the entire trip from launch to landing. Assuming the launch and landing happen at the same height, the time up will equal the time down. Students can then use equations to determine the launch speed.

Various types of launchers can be used. Several science equipment suppliers make devices that can shoot a marble straight up, and toys such as Stomp Rockets also work well.

Time to Set Up: <1 h
Time in Lab: 1 h
Performance Assessment

It is very important that students wear goggles when launching the objects.

Check the experiments for safety considerations before allowing students to do any experimentation.

_____

_____

_____

_____

_____

Data Collected

Record all your data in appropriate charts in the space below. Include any graphs in this space, as well.

Conclusion

Use your data/graphs to determine the launch velocity.

_____

_____

_____

_____

_____

Sources of Error

List two sources of error and what effect they have on your results.

Possible sources of error include:

• Difficulty determining when to start and stop the timer

• Not launching from the same height at which it lands

• Not launching the object straight upward

• Air resistance

Chapter 4: Motion in Two Dimensions • Vector Addition

Chapter 4 Lab Fenwick's Wild Ride

Purpose

In this lab, you will learn about vector addition by adding vectors graphically.

Materials

- map (following page)
- scissors
- protractor
- calculator

Discussion

There are two types of quantities in physics: scalars and vectors. Scalars are fully described by a number and a unit. Time is a scalar and requires only a number and unit, for example, 3 seconds. Sometimes, a scalar is not enough to fully describe a quantity. A vector quantity adds another piece of information—direction. To fully describe a vector, you must include a number, unit, and direction. In this laboratory, you will use vectors to follow physics student Fenwick as he travels around his home town of Centerville.

Procedure

1. On the next page is a map of Centerville and a ruler. Use scissors to cut out the ruler.

2. Locate Fenwick's home on the map. This is where he will start from. He has called a cab and is using GPS to tell his cab driver where to go.

3. Fenwick tells the cabbie he wants to go somewhere about 12.5 miles from home. Where does he want to go?

   Students may guess at a location, but you really cannot tell with just the

   distance given.

4. If you had trouble answering question 3, what other information would help the cabbie find the place Fenwick wants to go to?

   You would need the direction, as well.

5. Fenwick now tells the cabbie that he wants to go 12.5 miles, 340°. Where does Fenwick want to go?

   Fenwick wants to go to the newspaper.

Time to Set Up: <1 h
Time in Lab: <1 h
Quantitative Lab

The ruler is on the same sheet as the map, so the scale remains the same if the map is photocopied. If some students finish before others, you could challenge them to come up with another vector path through the town. Perhaps you could have them determine the route Fenwick would need to take in order to prepare for a date or dance.

Name _____ Period _____ Date _____

Map of
Centerville

Miles

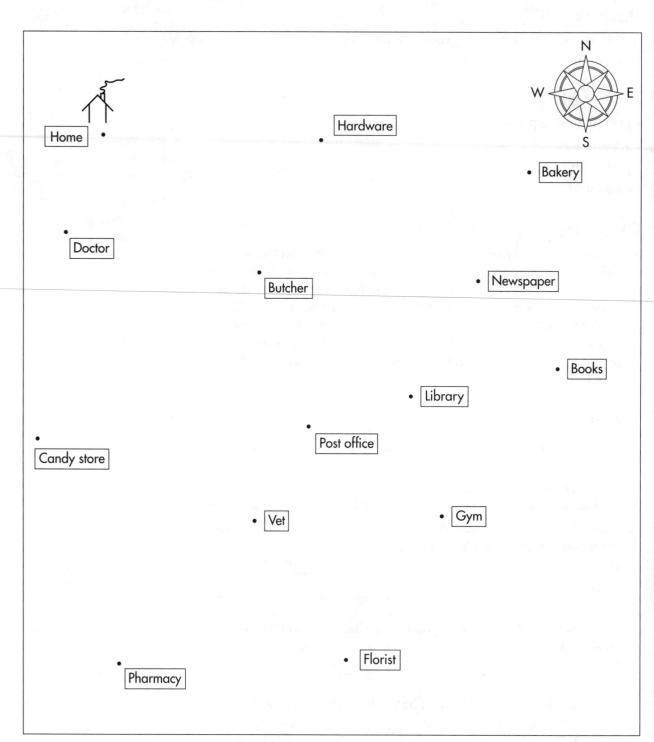

6. Draw an arrow on your map that starts at home and points directly to the place Fenwick wants to go to. This is a vector! The length of the vector represents the magnitude (number), and the arrow points in the direction. We use a scale to provide the units.

7. How far did Fenwick travel in the *x*-direction? Was it in the positive or negative *x*-direction?

   +11.7 miles

8. How far did Fenwick travel in the *y*-direction? Was it in the positive or negative *y*-direction?

   -4.3 miles

   The answers to 7 and 8 are the *x*- and *y*-components of the vector.

9. From this location, Fenwick asks the cabbie to take him 12 miles, 248°. Where is he going?

   He is going to the florist.

10. Draw this vector on your map.

11. Fenwick gives the cab driver the following vectors to be traveled one after the other. Draw arrows on the map to represent the vectors.

    Leg 3: 7 miles, 181°

    Leg 4: 9.2 miles, 48°

    Leg 5: 10.8 miles, 128°

    Pharmacy, post office, home

Analysis and Conclusions

1. Where does Fenwick end up after all five legs of his ride? This is his net displacement. Write this as a vector.

   He ends up at home, 0 miles, 0°.

2. For the entire ride, what was the total distance traveled?

   51.5 miles

3. Was Fenwick's net displacement the same as his total distance? Explain your answer.

   No, it is not the same. Displacement is a vector and includes direction.

   Distance is a scalar, so we don't need to worry about direction.

4. Locate where Fenwick was at the end of his second leg. If Fenwick had chosen to go here first, what vector would he have given the cab driver?

   17 miles, 295°

5. What are the *x*- and *y*- components for the vector you wrote in step 4?

   x: +7.2 miles; *y*: −15.4 miles

6. Determine the x- and y-components for the first two legs of the ride and write them in the chart below.

Ride leg	x-component	y-component
1	+11.7	−4.3
2	−4.5	−11.1

7. Considering that these two legs are connected, find the net x- and y-components for the two legs together.

$x = +7.2$ miles; $y = −15.4$ miles

8. Compare your answers for steps 5 and 7 above. Explain any similarities or differences.

These answers are the same. The final displacement is the vector sum of the two displacements.

9. Determine the components for the first four legs of Fenwick's ride and place those values in the table below. Also, determine the net components.

Ride leg	x-component	y-component
1	+11.7	−4.3
2	−4.5	−11.1
3	−7.0	−0.1
4	+6.2	+6.8

10. Find the total x- and y-components for the ride from home to the end of leg 4.

x: +6.4 miles; y: −8.7 miles

11. Without doing any calculations, predict what the components are for leg 5. Explain how you did this.

x: −6.4 miles, y: +8.7 miles. Because Fenwick ends up at home, his net

x- and y-components must be 0.

Chapter 4 Lab   Relative Motion

Purpose

In this lab, you will measure the velocity of a toy car in different frames of reference. You will also learn how two motions, one perpendicular to the other, affect each other.

Materials

- constant-velocity car
- meter stick
- stopwatch
- 2 m length of butcher paper
- marking pen
- masking tape

Discussion

How we describe the motion of an object depends on our frame of reference. A frame of reference may be thought of as the backdrop against which motion is observed and measured. Frequently, we choose the earth, and things attached to it, as our frame of reference, but this is not always the case. For example, as a passenger boards an airplane, the plane's cabin instantly replaces the earth as a frame of reference. During a smooth night flight, it's often difficult to tell that everything on the plane is traveling at high speed relative to the earth. On a grander scale, astronomers select distant stars as the backdrop for studying the motion of planets and other heavenly bodies.

Procedure

1. Use a meter stick and marking pen to draw a 1.5-m-long line on the butcher paper. Mark one end of the line "A" and the other "B."

2. Place two pieces of masking tape on the floor 1.5 m apart. Mark one piece "C" and the other "D."

C   D

A _____ B

Time to Set Up: <1 h
Time in Lab: 1 h
Quantitative Lab

Constant-velocity cars are inexpensive and readily available from toy stores and distributors of science education equipment. Many constant-velocity cars have speeds that make measurements in this lab difficult. To decrease the speed of a car, remove the battery cover and take out one of the batteries. Replace the battery with a wooden dowel covered with aluminum foil or with just a wad of aluminum foil.

Name _____ Period _____ Date _____

It is not necessary for the students to pull the paper at exactly the same speed as the car as long as the speeds are relatively close. The primary goal of the lab is to show that the velocities of the car and butcher paper combine vectorially.

3. Place the car at A so that it will move to B.

4. Measure the time required for the car to travel the length of the line. Repeat three times, and record the distance and times in Data Table 1.

5. Practice pulling the butcher paper from C to D along the floor at a constant speed about the same as that of the car. Using this speed, measure the time required for the butcher paper to travel from C to D along the floor. Repeat three times, and record the distance and times in Data Table 2.

6. Line up A on the paper with C on the floor. Place the front bumper of the car at A. Start pulling the butcher paper to D with the speed used in step 5 at the same time as your lab partner releases the car, so that it moves toward B. With both the car and the butcher paper moving, measure the time required for the car to travel from C to D. Repeat two times, and record the distance and times in Data Table 3.

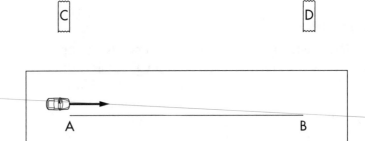

7. While pulling the butcher paper from C to D with the speed used in step 5, release the car with its front bumper at B so that it moves toward A. After 5 seconds, note the location of the car relative to the floor. Measure the distance from B to this point. Repeat two times, and record the distances and time in Data Table 4.

8. Place the car with its front bumper at A so that it will move toward B. Line up A with C and B with D. Pull the paper with the same speed as before, but this time perpendicular to the AB line.

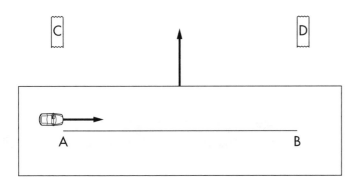

9. Repeat step 8 and allow the car to travel to point B on the paper. Determine the time it takes the car to travel from A to B. Mark the point where the car is, relative to the floor, when it reaches point B on the paper. Call this location "E." Measure the distance from C to E. Repeat two times, and record your data in Data Table 1.

Data

Data Table 1			
Trial	Distance (m)	Time (s)	Speed (m/s)
1			
2			
3			

Average speed _____

Data Table 2			
Trial	Distance (m)	Time (s)	Speed (m/s)
1			
2			
3			

Average speed _____

Data Table 3			
Trial	Distance (m)	Time (s)	Speed (m/s)
1			
2			
3			

Average speed _____

Data Table 4			
Trial	Distance (m)	Time (s)	Speed (m/s)
1			
2			
3			

Average speed _____

Data Table 5			
Trial	Distance from C to E (m)	Time (s)	Speed (m/s)
1			
2			
3			

Average speed _____

Analysis

1. Calculate the speed of the car based on the data in Data Tables 1, 2, and 3. Enter the calculated speeds for the three trials in the appropriate data tables.
2. Find the average of the three speeds in each of the data tables and enter it in the spaces provided.

Conclusions

1. What happens to the speed of the car relative to you, the observer, when it is placed on butcher paper moving in the same direction as the car?
   The two speeds combine to give a speed relative to you, the observer, that is equal to the sum of the car's and the butcher paper's speeds.

2. Describe the motion of the car relative to the table top when the car moves with the same speed as the butcher paper, but in the opposite direction.

The two speeds combine to give a speed relative to you, the observer, that is less

than the speed of either the car or the butcher paper. This speed may be zero.

3. State a rule that describes how the speeds of the car and butcher paper combine when the car is moving (a) in the same direction as the butcher paper and (b) in a direction opposite to that of the butcher paper.

The speeds add when you pull the paper in the same direction as the car is traveling

and subtract when you pull in the opposite direction.

4. How is the time required for the car to travel from A to B affected if the butcher paper is pulled perpendicular to the car's motion on the paper?

The time required for the car to cross the butcher paper is not affected by pulling the

paper in a direction perpendicular to the car's motion.

5. What effect does the motion of the butcher paper have on the path of the car relative to you?

The car travels along a line that is the vector sum of the two motions.

6. When the car travels perpendicular to the motion of the butcher paper, how does the motion of the butcher paper affect the car's speed relative to the (a) butcher paper and (b) the table top?

The car's speed relative to the butcher paper is unaffected. The car's speed relative to

the table top is greater than the car's speed relative to the butcher paper.

Chapter 4 Lab   Projectile Motion

Purpose

In this lab, you will determine the initial velocity of a projectile and learn how launch angle affects a projectile's range.

Discussion

A projectile is any object that, once launched by some force, moves through space solely under the influence of gravity. A baseball flying through the air may come to mind when the term projectile is mentioned. Strictly speaking, such objects are not exactly in projectile motion because air resistance also acts on the ball. That said, objects for which the effects of air resistance are negligible, such as the ball used in this lab, are generally thought of as projectiles.

In this lab, you will first determine the initial velocity of a projectile as it leaves a launcher. You will then determine how the angle of launch affects a projectile's range.

Materials

• projectile launcher and ball
• plumb line
• white paper
• carbon paper
• metric measuring tape

Procedure 🌀

Part A: Determining the Initial Velocity of a Projectile

1. Securely clamp the projectile launcher to the edge of a table.

2. Set the angle of the launcher to zero. This will result in a horizontal launch.

3. If the spring setting on your launcher is adjustable, select a setting. Record this setting in the data section.

4. Measure and record the vertical distance between the end of the launcher's barrel and the floor.

5. Attach a plumb line to the end of the launcher's barrel. This line should extend from the end of the barrel to the floor. Mark where the plumb line meets the floor.

6. Insert the ball in the launcher and fire one shot to determine approximately where the ball will land.

Time to Set Up: <1 h
Time in Lab: 1 h
Quantitative Lab

A wide variety of projectile launchers may be used. The launcher selected should produce a consistent initial velocity for all angles of launch.

Safety

Students should wear safety glasses when operating the launcher or when others are operating the launcher. Students should clear the area in front of the launcher prior to firing the projectile.

You may wish students to use a level to ensure that the launcher is parallel to the floor.

The launcher may have several spring settings. It is suggested that you select a setting that results in a range of approximately 2 m. Lower settings often produce fluctuating launch velocities.

7. Using tape, attach the piece of white paper to the floor at the point where the ball landed in step 6. Place and attach a piece of carbon paper, with its carbon side down, on top of the paper.

8. Fire the launcher five times. Each shot will result in a mark on the white paper.

9. Measure the distance from the mark made in step 5 to each of the marks on the paper. Enter these distances in Data Table 1.

Part B: Determining the Range of a Projectile

1. Place the launcher on the floor and mark its position with masking tape.

2. While keeping the launcher's position and spring setting constant, launch the projectile at an angle of 15°. Have your lab partner note and mark the point where the projectile lands.

For a simple calculation of range to be performed, it is necessary that the ball land at the same height at which it was launched.

3. Place a box or other object that provides a flat surface at the same height as the end of the launcher's barrel at the point where the projectile landed in step 2.

4. Launch the ball again and note where it lands on the box.

5. Measure the range from the end of the barrel of the launcher to the spot noted in step 3.

6. Repeat steps 4 and 5 four more times, and enter in Data Table 2 and calculate the average range.

7. Repeat steps 1 through 5 for launch angles of 30°, 45°, 60°, and 75°. Enter data from these launches in Data Tables 3 through 6.

Data

Spring setting _____

Vertical distance: _____ m

Data Table 1: Launch Angle 0°	
Trial	Measured range (m)
1	
2	
3	
4	
5	

Average range _____

v (speed of projectile) _____

| Data Table 2: Launch Angle 15° ||
Trial	Measured range (m)
1	
2	
3	
4	
5	

Average range _____

| Data Table 3: Launch Angle 30° ||
Trial	Measured range (m)
1	
2	
3	
4	
5	

Average range _____

| Data Table 4: Launch Angle 45° ||
Trial	Measured range (m)
1	
2	
3	
4	
5	

Average range _____

Data Table 5: Launch Angle 60°	
Trial	**Measured range (m)**
1	
2	
3	
4	
5	

Average range _____

Data Table 6: Launch Angle 75°	
Trial	**Measured range (m)**
1	
2	
3	
4	
5	

Average range _____

Analysis

1. Using the time of flight as determined by the equation $t = \sqrt{(2h/g)}$ and the average range from Data Table 1, calculate the initial velocity v_0 of the ball.

2. Enter the initial velocity v_0 in Data Table 7.

3. Enter the average range for each launch angle into Data Table 7.

4. Calculate the theoretical range for each launch angle using $R = \left(\dfrac{2v_0^2}{g}\right)\sin\theta\cos\theta$ and enter in Data Table 7.

5. Using the theoretical value of the range as the accepted value, calculate the percent error in the range for each launch angle.

Data Table 7				
Angle of launch (°)	**v_0 (m/s)**	**R (measured) (m)**	**R (theoretical) (m)**	**% error in measured range**
15				
30				
45				
60				
75				

Conclusions

1. Make a graph of range versus launch angle.

2. Which angle of launch resulted in the greatest range?

   A launch angle of 45°produces the greatest range.

3. Do any of the launch angles produce the same range? Explain why you think this is so.

   Complementary angles, such as 30° and 60°, produce the same range.

4. Discuss sources of error.

   Errors could have been introduced when setting the launch angle and measuring the

   projectile's range. Inconsistencies in the projectile's initial velocity and in positioning

   the launcher on the table and the floor may have also been sources of error.

Chapter 4: Motion in Two Dimensions • Performance Task

Chapter 4 Lab   X Marks the Spot

Your Task

You must predict the exact location where the projectile will land. The projectile will be launched from the table at an angle. You will have time to design the experiment and then test your launcher. Your instructor will give you the angle of the launch just prior to the prediction.

Time to Set Up: <1 h
Time in Lab: 1 h
Performance Assessment

Equipment Provided

- projectile launcher
- projectile

There are several models of projectile launchers on the market. This lab may be challenging because the projectile is shot from an angle and off a table.

Requirements

- You must design an experiment to solve the problem.
- You may request additional equipment from your instructor.
- Your instructor must approve your method BEFORE you begin experimenting.
- You MAY NOT launch the projectile *from the table* until you try to hit the target.
- When ready, request an angle from your instructor. You will then have 5 minutes to set up your launcher and place your X on the floor.
- Show calculations/graphs used to solve the problem, if applicable.
- List at least two sources of error. For each, indicate what effect the error would have on your results.

Procedure Followed

List your procedure as a set of steps that another student in the class could easily follow.

Students will most likely ask for meter sticks and stopwatches. They can

determine the launch velocity by launching the projectile straight up. They

should also measure the height of the table.

_____

_____

_____

_____

_____

_____

_____

Data Collected

Record all your data in appropriate charts in the space below. Include any graphs in this space, as well.

Encourage students to do several trials with the launcher from the ground before attempting to hit their spot.

Conclusion

Use your data/graphs to determine where to place the X on the floor.
Students should show their calculations in this section.

_____

_____

_____

_____

_____

Outcome

How far from the center of the X did your projectile land?

_____

Sources of Error

Possible sources of error include:

• Inconsistent launch velocities

• Floors not level

• Not taking into account the height of the projectile above the table top at

  launch

Chapter 5: Newton's Laws of Motion • Applying Newton's Laws

Chapter 5 Lab   Hanging Around

Purpose
In this lab, you will explore the forces acting on objects at rest.

Time to Set Up: 1 h
Time in Lab: <1 h
Quantitative Lab

Materials
- 500 g masses
- string
- ringstands
- washer
- right-angle clamps
- newton scales

- meter stick
- protractor
- eye hooks
- unknown mass
- C clamps

Discussion
All the objects in this lab will be at rest. What can you say about the net force acting on an object at rest? You know that if you drop a mass it will not remain stationary. Yet, on a table or hung from a rope, the same mass will remain at rest. In these cases, forces other than gravity must be present. Surfaces are capable of exerting forces, and so are strings or ropes. We call these forces normal forces and tensions, respectively.

Students can start at any station and rotate until they complete all six stations.

Station 1: A Hanging Mass
What is the net force acting on the mass?

The net force is 0.
_____

What evidence can you give to support this claim?

The mass is not moving.
_____

_____

Draw a force diagram for the mass.

What is the weight of the mass?

5 N
_____

Equipment
Ringstand, C clamp, string, newton scale, 500 g mass

Scale

Equipment
Two ringstands, two right-angle clamps, metal bar, string, two newton scales, 500 g mass

Assembly
Use the right-angle clamps to secure the metal bar horizontally between the ring stands. Tie one end of each string to a scale and the other end to the bar loosely enough so that students can slide the string back and forth along the bar.

Station 2: Another Hanging Mass

A. Make the strings as far apart as possible.

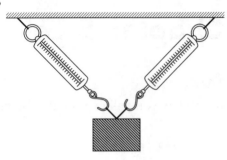

What is the net force acting on the mass?

The net force is 0.

What evidence can you give to support this claim?

The mass is at rest.

Draw a force diagram for the mass. Include values for known forces.

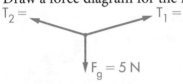

$T_2 = $ ⟵ ⟶ $T_1 = $

$F_g = 5\,N$

B. Now bring the strings in closer together.
What is the net force acting on the mass?

~~The net force is 0.~~

Draw a force diagram for the mass. Include values for known forces.

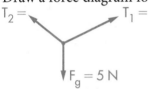

$T_2 = $ $T_1 = $

$F_g = 5\,N$

What changed from situation A to situation B?

The angle made by the strings changed.

How do the scale readings compare between the two situations?

When the strings were farther apart, the scale readings were larger.

Station 3: A Hanging System

Equipment
Two ringstands, two right-angle clamps, two newton scales, meter stick, cup hooks, two 500 g masses

Assembly
Screw the cup hooks into the meter stick as shown in the diagram so that you can change the location of the mass and the scales. Students should ignore the weight of the meter stick.

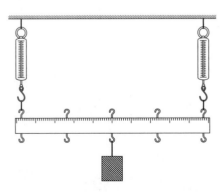

Two scales are used to support the meter stick system. Place the scales at the ends of the meter stick.
What do the scales read?

Each scale should read 2.5 N.

Draw a force diagram for the meter stick.

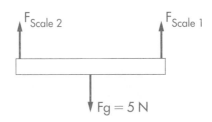

$F_g = 5\ N$

Now move one scale closer to the middle of the meter stick.
What do the scales read now?

The scale closer to the middle will have a higher reading, but they still total

5 N.

Draw a force diagram for this new system.

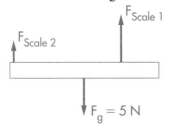

$F_g = 5\ N$

Return the scale to the end of the meter stick. Add an additional mass to the hanging system.
What do the scales read now?

Each scale should read 5 N.

Make a generalization about what you learned at this station.

The scale readings added together should equal the total weight pulling

down on the meter stick.

_____

Equipment
Two ringstands, three newton scales, two 500 g masses, C clamps

Assembly
Use the C clamps to secure the ringstands to the table. Hang the newton scales as shown, from the ringstands. Zero the scales so the reading on the top scale does not include the weight of the bottom scale.

Station 4: Two Are Better Than One?

The two hanging masses are identical. Note the readings on the scales.
Explain your observations.

All the scales should read 5 N. All the scales are at

rest, so they all have a net force of 0. They all get

pulled downward with a force of 5 N (because we

are neglecting the weight of the second scale), so

they must also experience an upward pull of 5 N.

Now hang a second mass from string A.
Predict the reading on both scales on string b if you add the same mass to that system.
Prediction:

_____

Check it out! Were you right?

_____

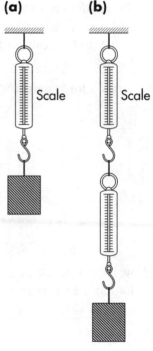

(a)   (b)

Scale   Scale

Equipment:
Protractor, large washer, string, three C clamps, three newton scales

Assembly
Tie three strings to the washer. Secure the three newton scales to the table using the C clamps. Tie the three strings from the washer to the three newton scales so that the washer is in equilibrium and each scale has a reading.

Station 5: Force Table

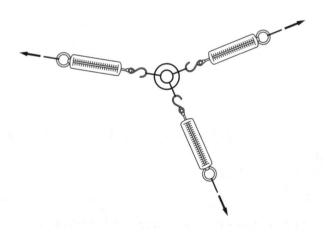

Using the scale readings and a protractor, draw a force diagram for the horizontal forces acting on the washer. Mathematically prove that the net force on the washer is 0.

Using a scale drawing or trigonometry, students should see that the three

x-components and the three *y*-components add up to 0.

_____

_____

_____

Station 6: A Hanging Mass

Draw a force diagram for the hanging mass.

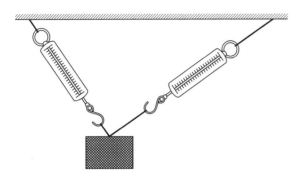

Equipment
Protractor, string, two newton scales, unknown mass

Assembly
Hang the unknown mass from the ceiling using two pieces of string at different angles, with a newton scale measuring the tension for each string.

Determine the mass of the hanging object.

$T_2 =$ ___ $T_1 =$ ___

θ_2 θ_1

$F_{g \text{ or } W}$

Students should find the *y*-components of the tension for each string. Their

sum will equal the unknown weight.

Chapter 5: Newton's Laws of Motion • Newton's First Law of Motion

Chapter 5 Lab   Kick Disks to the Rescue

Purpose

In this lab, you will answer the question: Is an object necessarily at rest if the net force acting on it is zero?

Materials

• small hovercraft

Discussion

By now, you should believe that if an object is at rest, the net force on that object must be zero. Today, we will try to see if the converse of this statement is true. That is, if the net force on an object is zero, is it at rest?

Why use a low-friction device such as a kick disk? When we lift an object off the floor or table, we remove the force the table exerts on the object. With the kick disk, the air pushing on the object exerts an upward force equal in magnitude to the downward force of gravity.

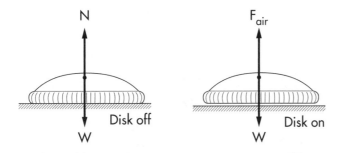

Why does it matter if the disk is off the table? Because when the disk is not in direct contact with the table, the force of friction acting on the disk is negligible.

Be careful when drawing force diagrams. Once you are no longer touching an object, you are not exerting a force on that object!

Procedure

Part A: With the Kick Disk Off

1. Place the disk on the floor or table. What is the net force acting on the disk? How do you know? Draw a force diagram for this situation.

$\uparrow F_N$

$\downarrow F_g$

The net force is 0 because the disk is

at rest.

_____

_____

Time to Set Up: <1 h
Time in Lab: 1 h
Qualitative Lab

This lab uses battery-operated hovercrafts. You can purchase them from most science supply stores.

2. Now give the disk a push. Discuss the motion of the disk while you are pushing on it. Draw a force diagram for this situation.

The disk speeds up in the direction it is pushed.

3. Stop pushing the disk. Describe the motion of the disk. Draw a force diagram for this situation.

When the pushing stops, the disk should slow down and eventually stop.

Students may see the disk move a bit, especially if the floors are not level.

Part B: With the Disk Turned On

1. Place the disk on the floor or table. What is the net force acting on the disk? How do you know? Draw a force diagram for this situation.

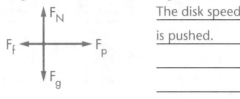

The net force is zero; the disk should be at rest.

2. Now give the disk a push. *While you are pushing*, discuss the motion of the disk. Draw a force diagram for this situation.

The disk speeds up in the direction it is pushed.

3. Stop pushing the disk. Describe the motion of the disk. Draw a force diagram for this situation.

The disk should continue at a constant speed in a straight line.

Analysis and Conclusions

1. Compare the force diagrams for the two parts. How do they differ?

   When the disk is off, there is a normal force and therefore friction. When the disk is

   on, the force of the air supports the disk, making friction negligible.

2. Which of your diagrams showed a net force equal to zero? Describe the motion of
   the disk in each situation.

   Part A, step 1: at rest

   Part B, step 1: at rest

   Part B, step 3: constant velocity

3. If there is no net force acting on an object, is the object necessarily at rest?

   No, because in Part B, step 3, the disk had a net force of 0 and was moving at a

   constant speed in a straight line

Chapter 5 Lab   Newton's Second Law of Motion

Time to Set Up: <1 h
Time in Lab: 1 h
Quantitative Lab

Purpose

In this lab, you will use a motion detector to determine the acceleration of a cart when (1) the net force applied to the cart increases, but the mass of the system remains constant; and (2) the net force applied to the cart stays constant, but the mass of the system is changed.

Discussion

Newton's first law of motion tells us that without an external net force an object at rest will remain at rest, or, if moving, will keep moving in the same direction at a constant speed. But what happens when a net force acts on an object? In this lab, you will carry out an investigation to determine the relationship between net force, mass, and acceleration.

Materials

- dynamics cart
- track
- motion detector
- low-friction pulley
- meter stick
- mass set
- mass hanger
- 1 m length of string

Procedure ⚠

Part A: Variable Force, Constant Mass

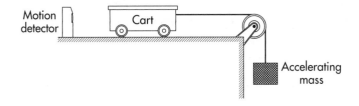

Have students adjust the position of the pulley so that the string is level with the track. Remind students to catch the mass hanger and masses when they are dropped; do not allow them to crash to the floor.

1. Level the track.

2. Place the motion detector on one end of the track, as shown in the picture above. Adjust the motion sensor so that it points parallel to the track.

3. After attaching the pulley to the other end of the track, place this end of the track beyond the edge of the table.

4. Determine the mass of the cart and mass hanger. Enter the sum of these masses in Data Table 1.

5. Attach one end of the string to the mass hanger, the other end to the cart.

6. Place the cart on the track near the motion detector and place the string over the pulley. The mass hanger should be suspended from the string, as shown in the figure. Place five 10 g slotted masses on the cart.

7. Turn on the computer and access the velocity versus time graph.

8. When you are ready to release the cart, start recording data. Right before the cart hits the end of the track, stop recording data. Make certain someone is at the end of the track to stop the cart.

9. To determine the cart's acceleration, use the slope tool to find the slope of the region of the graph corresponding to accelerated motion. Record this acceleration in Data Table 1.

10. Repeat the above process five times, each time moving an additional 10 g mass from the cart to the hanger until all masses are on the hanger. By moving the mass from the cart to the hanger, the total mass of the system remains unchanged but the accelerating force increases.

Part B: Constant Force, Variable Mass

1. Repeat the procedure as above. However, this time the mass hanger will remain empty for all trials.

2. For each trial, add an additional 100 g mass to the cart. Do this for five trials.

Data

Mass of Cart _____ kg
Mass of Empty Hanger ____ kg

Data Table 1				
Trial	Suspended mass (kg)	Applied force (N)	Total mass of cart and suspended mass (kg)	Acceleration (m/s²)
1				
2				
3				
4				
5				

Data Table 2				
Trial	Suspended mass (kg)	Applied force (N)	Total mass of cart and suspended mass (kg)	Acceleration (m/s²)
1				
2				
3				
4				
5				

Analysis

1. Calculate the applied force in Parts A and B and enter in Data Tables 1 and 2, respectively. Remember, the force of gravity on the hanging mass is the applied force.

2. Calculate the total mass of the cart and suspended mass in Parts A and B and enter in Data Tables 1 and 2, respectively.

Conclusions

1. Draw a force diagram for the cart.

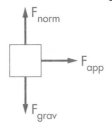

2. Using the data in Data Table 1, plot a graph of acceleration versus net force.

3. What is the relationship between the acceleration and the net force?
   The acceleration is directly proportional to the net force.

4. Plot a graph of acceleration versus total mass from the data in Data Table 2.

5. What is the relationship between the acceleration and the total mass?

The acceleration is inversely proportional to the total mass.

6. Combine the statements from steps 3 and 5 above into a single mathematical relationship involving net force, mass, and acceleration.

The results of the experiment indicate that the acceleration of the cart is directly

proportional to the net force and inversely proportional to the mass being

accelerated. Mathematically stated: $a \propto F_{net}/m$.

Chapter 5 Lab   Cart Push

Time to Set Up: <1 h
Time in Lab: 1 h
Quantitative Lab

Purpose

In this lab, you will apply Newton's second law in order to determine the mass of a student and a lab cart.

Materials

- cart
- bathroom scale
- meter stick
- stopwatch

Scooters, skateboards, and castered chairs work well in this lab. The activity should be done well away from hard edges, such as those of lab furniture. If a skateboard is used, riders should wear safety protection as recommended by skateboard manufacturers.

Discussion

Newton's second law states that an object's acceleration is directly proportional to the net force acting on the object and inversely proportional to the object's mass. Stated mathematically, $a = F_{net}/m$. If the net force and acceleration of the object are in the same direction, this equation can be rearranged to give an expression for the mass: $m = F_{net}/a$. Thus, if an object is pushed with a known net force and the object's acceleration is measured, the mass can be calculated from this relationship.

In this lab, you will use Newton's second law to determine the mass of a classmate and cart by measuring the acceleration of the rider and cart produced by a force applied with a bathroom scale.

The principal goal of this lab is to demonstrate a large-scale application of Newton's second law. The errors in the values obtained for the combined mass of the rider and cart may be considerable. This should not be a concern, because in this lab the result is not as important as the process.

Procedure ⚠

1. Decide who will be the rider, the "accelerator," the time keeper, and the data recorder.

2. While the rider holds the cart, determine their combined weight in pounds using a bathroom scale. Enter this weight in the data section.

3. Use strips of masking tape to mark the start and finish of a 10-m-long path on a hallway floor.

4. Align the front end of the cart with the first strip of tape.

5. After the rider has been comfortably seated on the cart, group members should carry out the following sequence of actions:

   a. The accelerator positions the bathroom scale on the rider's back. All pushing must be done horizontally.

   b. The accelerator determines the force of friction acting on the cart by measuring the force needed to keep the cart and rider moving with a constant speed. This force, which has the same value for all trials, is recorded as the frictional force.

   c. The timer starts the stopwatch and, simultaneously, the accelerator begins to apply a constant horizontal force greater than the frictional force to the scale and back of the rider.

   d. The time keeper stops the stopwatch when the front end of the cart reaches the strip of tape marking 10 m. Enter applied force and time in Data Table 1. Repeat three more times.

Data

Weight of cart and rider as measured on bathroom scale _____ lb
Frictional force acting on cart and rider _____ lb

Table 1 Data		
Trial	Force applied to cart and rider (lb)	Time (s)
1		
2		
3		
4		

Average time _____

Analysis

1. Using $v_{avg} = d/t$, calculate the average velocity of the cart and rider during the acceleration. Enter values in Data Table 2.

2. Using $v_{avg} = (v_0 + v_f)/2$, calculate the final velocity of the cart and rider. Enter values in Data Table 2.

3. Using $a = (v_f - v_0)/t$, calculate the acceleration of the cart and rider. Enter values in Data Table 2.

4. Calculate F_{net} by subtracting $F_{friction}$ from $F_{applied}$. Enter values in Data Table 2.

5. Convert the net force from pounds to newtons using 4.45 N/lb.

6. Calculate the experimental mass of the cart and rider using $m = F_{net}/a$. Enter this value in Data Table 2.

7. Multiply the weight of the cart and rider by 0.45 kg/lb to obtain the equivalent mass in kilograms. Enter this value as the actual mass in Data Table 2.

8. Compute the percent error in the experimental value for the mass of the rider and cart.

Table 2 Data										
Trial	v_{avg} (m/s)	v_f (m/s)	a (m/s^2)	$F_{applied}$ (lb)	$F_{friction}$ (lb)	F_{net} (lb)	F_{net} (N)	Actual mass (kg)	Experimental mass (kg)	% error
1										
2										
3										
4										

Conclusions

1. What effect would increasing the applied force have on the acceleration of the rider and cart?

   If the applied force were increased, the acceleration would also increase.

   _____

2. List three sources of error in this experiment.

   It is difficult to maintain a consistent applied force, push exactly horizontally,

   determine when the cart is moving at a constant speed during the determination of

   the frictional force.

Chapter 5 Lab   Finding the Mass of the Block

Your Task

Using what you know about Newton's laws and frictional forces, determine the mass of the unknown block.

Equipment Provided

• Block of wood

Requirements

• You must design an experiment to solve the problem.

• You may request additional equipment from your instructor.

• You will submit an equipment list and procedure before taking any data.

• You will only get one chance to ask for equipment. Make sure your list is complete.

• Your procedure should be thorough enough that another student in the class could follow your instructions.

• Present your data in tables, if appropriate.

• Show calculations used to solve the problem, if applicable.

• List at least two sources of error. For each, indicate the effect the error would have on your results.

Equipment Requested

Students may request newton scales, known masses, string, motion

detectors, force probes, a known block of wood, and so on.

_____

_____

_____

_____

Time to Set Up: <1 h
Time in Lab: 1 h
Performance Assessment

Provide students with a block of wood about 4″ × 6″ that has a hook on one end so they can drag the block across a surface.

It is imperative that students involve friction in their determination of the mass.

Procedure Followed

Students will first need to determine the coefficient of friction between the
wood and the surface, using a known mass. They may pull another block
of wood at a constant velocity to determine the force of friction. They can
then find the frictional force on the unknown block and use that value to
determine its mass.

_____

_____

_____

_____

_____

Data Collected

Conclusion

_____

_____

_____

_____

Sources of Error

Possible sources of error include:

• Not pulling the block at a constant velocity.

• Failing to pull the block exactly horizontally.

• Error in reading the scale as it is moving.

• The coefficient of friction between the table surface and the wood block
  might vary.

Chapter 6 Lab   Energy of a Pendulum

Purpose

In this lab, you will measure and compare changes in the gravitational potential energy and the kinetic energy of a pendulum bob during its motion.

Discussion

The mechanical energy of an object, such as a pendulum bob, is defined as the sum of its potential and kinetic energies. When a pendulum bob is displaced to one side, its vertical height above the lowest point of its motion is increased by an amount equal to Δh This increases the bob's gravitational potential energy by an amount equal to $mg\Delta h$ When the bob is released, its potential energy is transformed into kinetic energy, given by $\frac{1}{2}mv^2$. If the mechanical energy is constant during the motion of a pendulum, a decrease in gravitational potential energy should be accompanied by an equal increase in kinetic energy, and vice versa.

Materials

- pendulum bob
- cord
- ringstand
- support rod
- photogate and timer
- meter stick
- Vernier caliper

Figure 1

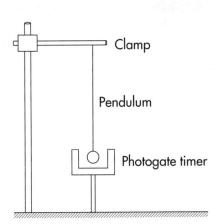

Time to Set Up: <1 h
Time in Lab: <1 h
Quantitative Lab

Encourage students to avoid hitting the photogate with the bob.

Procedure

1. Find the mass of the pendulum bob and record it in the data section.

2. Using a Vernier caliper, measure the diameter of the bob and record it in the data section.

3. Construct a pendulum as shown in Figure 1 by connecting the string to the bob and attaching the string to the support rod.

4. Position the photogate so that the bob is free to swing through it.

5. With the bob hanging freely, measure the distance between the center of the bob and the tabletop. Enter this distance as h_0 in Data Table 1.

6. Pull the bob back and make sure it passes through the photogate when it swings. Make sure that the pendulum is pulled back straight, with the string fully extended.

7. Pull the bob back again and have a lab partner measure the height of the center of the bob above the table top. Record this height as h in Data Table 1.

8. After activating the timer, release the pendulum. Have someone catch the pendulum on the other side of its swing. Do not allow the bob to pass through the photogate a second time.

9. The timer displays the time it took the bob to pass through the photogate. Record this time as Δt in Data Table 1.

10. Repeat steps 6 through 9 four more times using different initial heights of the bob.

Data

Mass of pendulum bob _____ kg

Diameter of pendulum bob _____ m

Data Table 1					
Trial	h_0 (m)	h (m)	Δh (m)	Δt (s)	v (m/s)
1					
2					
3					
4					
5					

Data Table 2		
Trial	ΔPE	ΔKE
1		
2		
3		
4		
5		

Analysis

1. For each trial, calculate the velocity of the bob as it passes through the photogate by dividing the bob's diameter by its time of passage through the photogate. Enter these values in Data Table 1.

2. For each trial, use $\Delta PE = mg\Delta h$ to calculate the change in the bob's potential energy (ΔPE) as it moves from its highest to its lowest point. Enter this in Data Table 2.

3. For each trial, use $\Delta KE = \frac{1}{2}mv^2$ to calculate the change in the bob's kinetic energy as it moves from its highest to its lowest point. Enter this in Data Table 2.

Conclusions

1. What happens to the bob's potential energy as it swings from the highest point to the lowest?

   The potential energy decreases.

2. What happens to the bob's kinetic energy as it swings from the highest point to the lowest?

   The kinetic energy increases.

3. How did the pendulum bob's change in potential energy compare to the change in kinetic energy as it moved from its highest point to its lowest point?

   The changes in energies should be the same or very similar, except that the potential

   energy change is negative, while the kinetic energy change is positive.

   What does this say about the bob's total mechanical energy as it goes through its motion?

   The bob's total mechanical energy is constant.

4. What do you think would to happen to the pendulum bob's mechanical energy if it were allowed to swing back and forth many times? Explain your answer.

Because there is friction in the system, the mechanical energy will decrease over time.

Chapter 6 Lab   Human Horsepower

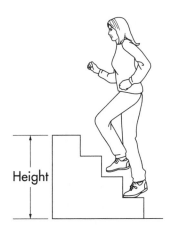

Height

Time to Set Up: <1 h
Time in Lab: 1 h
Quantitative Lab

Purpose

In this lab, you will determine the power produced, as measured in watts and horsepower, when you (a) walk up a flight of stairs, (b) jog up a flight of stairs, and (c) lift a 1 kg mass.

Discussion

Power is the rate at which work is done. The faster a given amount of work is done, the greater the power. In the metric system, with work measured in joules, power is expressed in joules per second. One joule per second is called a watt, named after engineer and inventor James Watt. Another frequently used unit of power is the horsepower. One horsepower is equivalent to 746 watts.

Materials

- meter stick
- stopwatch
- bathroom scale
- 1.3 m of cord
- 1 kg mass
- 30 cm length of 5-cm-diameter dowel rod

Procedure ⚠

Part A: Determining Power Produced by Legs

1. Go to a stairwell and measure the vertical distance, in meters, between two floors. This may be done by measuring the height of one step, counting the number of steps, and then multiplying the height

Students who have medical conditions that exclude them from participation in sports or physical education classes should not participate in the jogging portion of this experiment. The path of the joggers should be cleared before they ascend the stairs.

If students are not willing to use their actual weight, they can make up a weight for the experiment.

of one step by the total number of steps. Enter these distances in Data Table 1.

2. Using the bathroom scale, measure your weight in pounds. Record your weight in Data Tables 2 and 3.

3. Have a lab partner use the stopwatch to measure the time it takes you to walk up the stairs between the two floors. Enter this time in Data Table 2.

4. Have your lab partner measure the time it takes you to jog up the same flight of stairs to the higher floor. Enter this time in Data Table 3.

5. Steps 2 through 4 should be repeated by each member of the group.

Part B: Determining Power Produced by Hands

Assemble the apparatus before the students arrive. Secure the cord to the center of the dowel rod. Attach the 1 kg mass to the free end of the cord. Use a piece of tape to mark a point on the cord 1 m from the dowel rod.

1. Hold the dowel rod with hands on both sides of the cord. Start with the weight on the floor. Practice rolling the dowel in your hands so that the cord winds around it and lifts the mass.

2. When ready, place the mass on the floor again. Have a lab partner measure the time required for you to lift the mass through a distance of 1 meter (until the tape reaches the dowel rod). Record this time in Data Table 4.

3. Steps 1 and 2 should be repeated by each member of the group.

Data

Data Table 1
Distance between steps _____m
Number of steps _____ m
Distance between floors _____m

Data Table 2: Walking Data						
Name of student	Weight (lb)	Weight (N)	Time (s)	Work done (J)	Power (W)	Power (hp)

Data Table 3: Jogging Data						
Name of student	Weight (lb)	Weight (N)	Time (s)	Work done (J)	Power (W)	Power (hp)

Data Table 4: Lifting Data

Distance through which mass was moved: _____ m

Name of student	Weight of 1 kg mass (N)	Work done (J)	Time (s)	Power (W)	Power (hp)

Analysis

Part A

1. Calculate your weight in newtons, and that of your lab partners, by multiplying each weight in pounds by 4.45 N/lb.

2. Calculate the work done by you and your lab partners by multiplying weight in newtons by the vertical distance in meters between floors.

3. Use the definition of power, $P = W/t$, to calculate the power output in watts produced by you and members of your lab group.

4. Calculate the horsepower of each member of your group by dividing your power in watts by 746 watts/hp.

Part B

1. Determine the weight of the 1 kg mass in newtons.

2. Calculate the work done by each student in lifting the 1 kg mass to a height of 1 m.

3. Calculate the power output in watts produced by each student in lifting the 1 kg mass.

4. Calculate the horsepower produced by each student in lifting the 1 kg mass.

Conclusions

1. Which person from your lab group did the most work in Part A? Explain your answer.

   The person with the largest mass does the most work.

2. In Part A, who produced the most power? Explain your answer.

   Usually, this is the most massive person; however, a fast, less massive student can also be the most powerful.

3. In Part B, who from your lab group did the most work? Explain your answer.

   They all did the same work because they all lifted a 1 kg mass to a height of 1 m.

4. In Part B, who produced the most power? Explain your answer.

   The person who lifted the mass in the least time produced the most power.

5. Which activity, climbing the stairs or lifting the 1 kg mass, produced the greater amount of power? Explain why you think this is so.

   Climbing the stairs produced the greater amount of power because much more work was done.

6. How did your power output when jogging up the stairs compare to the power consumed by a 100 watt light bulb?

   A student jogging up a flight of stairs will produce several times the power consumed by a 100 watt light bulb.

Chapter 6: Work and Energy • Work and Energy

Chapter 6 Lab   Poppers

Your Task

You must determine the amount of work that is done when you turn the popper inside out.

Equipment Provided

• popper

Requirements

• You must design an experiment to solve the problem.
• You may request additional equipment from your instructor.
• Your instructor must approve your method BEFORE you begin experimenting.
• Show calculations/graphs used to solve the problem, if applicable.
• List at least two sources of error. For each, indicate what effect the error would have on your results.

Equipment Requested

Students might request rulers, meter sticks, stopwatches, and electronic

scales.

_____

_____

_____

Procedure Followed

List your procedure as a set of steps that another student in the class could easily follow.

Students will most likely use the fact that the work put into the popper

must equal the elastic energy stored in the popper. This then must equal

(assuming no frictional losses) the potential energy at the top of the

popper's path. Some students may choose to use the equation for work,

$W = F \times d$, but this does not generate good results because the force is very

difficult to measure. They might also attempt to deduce the popper's kinetic

Time to Set Up: <1 h
Time in Lab: 1 h
Performance Assessment

Poppers are sold in part stores and science supply stores. You could also use the kind with springs.

energy at takeoff by using the meter stick and a stopwatch to calculate its average speed while falling from the highest point. _____

_____

_____

Data Collected

Record all your data in appropriate charts in the space below. Include any graphs in this space as well.

Encourage students to do several trials and get an average amount of work.

Conclusion

Use your data/graphs to determine how much work was done when you turned the popper inside out.

Students should show their calculations in this section. _____

_____

_____

_____

_____

Sources of Error

Possible sources of error include: _____

• Loss of energy to sound, heat, and other forms due to frictional effects.

• Difficulty in measuring the popper's highest point. _____

• The popper may not pop straight up and therefore has some kinetic energy
   at the top.

• Inconsistencies in the amount the popper is turned inside out. _____

Chapter 7: Linear Momentum and Collisions • Conservation of Momentum

Chapter 7 Lab   Momentum Conservation

Purpose

In this lab, you will judge the relative velocities of carts and discover what conservation of momentum means.

Materials

- two carts
- masses to double the mass of a cart
- track
- masking tape

Discussion

Momentum is sometimes called inertia in motion. It is the product of an object's mass and its velocity. Momentum is a vector quantity, and direction is therefore an important factor when calculating an object's momentum. You will examine three different types of collisions in this lab. We will call them stick, bounce, and explode. To produce a stick collision, use tape so that the carts remain together after they hit. If the cars hit but do not stick together, this would be considered a bounce collision. Finally, push the carts together with the spring compressed between them and then release to create an explode collision.

Procedure

1. Place the track on a level surface.
2. You will be doing three different types of collisions in this lab. See the discussion above for instructions on how to produce each type of collision.
3. For each trial, add masses to the carts as indicated. Mass m indicates an empty cart; $2m$ indicates that a mass equal to the mass of the empty cart should be added to the cart.
4. Decide which direction you will call positive. If a cart moves in that direction, its velocity would be positive.
5. Practice the initial conditions for each trial before you allow the carts to collide.
6. For the final conditions, you are considering the velocity of the cart immediately following the collision relative to its initial velocity. Because you are only estimating the velocities, limit your answers for the "after" velocities to the following magnitudes: v, $v/2$, $v/3$, $4v/3$, $5v/3$, $2v/3$, $2v$, and 0. Don't forget to indicate the direction of

Time to Set Up: <1 h
Time in Lab: <1 h
Qualitative Lab

One of the carts must have a spring to allow for "explosions." A track is not absolutely necessary, but it will make the carts travel only in one line. Some carts come with Velcro strips to help them stick together during a totally inelastic collision. Many carts come with blocks that are exactly the same mass as the cart and make doubling the mass quite easy.

the velocity, using $+/-$. For example, if a cart has an initial velocity of v and after the collision it slows down and travels in the opposite direction, your choices for the final velocity are $-v/2$, $-v/3$, $-2v/3$.

7. Complete Data Table 1 for all trials.

Data Table 1								
Trial: Type of collision	Cart 1 before		Cart 2 before		Cart 1 after		Cart 2 after	
	Mass	Velocity	Mass	Velocity	Mass	Velocity	Mass	Velocity
1: Stick	m	$+v$	m	0	m	$+v/2$	m	$+v/2$
2: Stick	m	$+v$	m	$-v$	m	0	m	0
3: Stick	$2m$	$+v$	m	0	$2m$	$+2v/3$	m	$+2v/3$
4: Stick	m	$+v$	$2m$	0	m	$+v/3$	$2m$	$+v/3$
5: Stick	m	$+v$	$2m$	$-v$	m	$-v/3$	$2m$	$-v/3$
6: Stick	$2m$	$+v$	m	$-v$	$2m$	$+v/2$	m	$+v/2$
7: Bounce	m	$+v$	m	0	m	0	m	$+v$
8: Bounce	m	$+v$	m	$-v$	m	$-v$	m	$+v$
9: Bounce	$2m$	$+v$	m	$-v$	$2m$	$-v/3$	m	$+5v/3$
10: Bounce	$2m$	$+v$	m	0	$2m$	$+v/3$	m	$+4v/3$
11: Bounce	m	$+v$	$2m$	0	m	$-v/3$	$2m$	$+2v/3$
12: Explode	m	0	m	0	m	$-v$	m	$+v$
13: Explode	$2m$	0	m	0	$2m$	$-v/2$	m	$+v$
14: Explode	m	0	$2m$	0	m	$-v$	$2m$	$+v/2$

Analysis and Conclusions

1. Determine the momentum of each cart before and after the collision, using momentum = mass × velocity. Enter these values in Data Table 2.

2. Determine the total momentum in the system before the collision by adding the momenta of carts 1 and 2 before the collision. Enter these values in Data Table 2.

3. Determine the total momentum in the system after the collision by adding the momenta of carts 1 and 2 after the collision. Enter these values in Data Table 2.

4. For trials 1–6, how did the velocities of the carts compare after the collision?
   The velocities are the same. For a "stick" collision, the carts must have the same

   velocity because they are stuck together.

			Data Table 2			
Trial	Momentum of cart 1 before	Momentum of cart 2 before	Total momentum before	Momentum of cart 1 after	Momentum of cart 2 after	Total momentum after
1						
2						
3						
4						
5						
6						
7						
8						
9						
10						
11						
12						
13						
14						

5. For trials 12–14, what is the total momentum in the system before the collision? Why is this so?

When there is an explosion, both carts start at rest, so the total momentum in the system is 0.

6. For each trial, fill in Data Table 3.

7. Looking at Data Table 3, what can you say about the total momentum in a system that experiences a collision?

The total momentum in the system should remain constant.

8. Are there any trials that disagree with your answer to step 7? If so, offer an explanation of why that trial was different.

There may be a trial or two that do not show conservation of momentum. Students might have misjudged a velocity, especially when the cart slowed down.

Data Table 3		
Trial	Total momentum before collision	Total momentum after collision
1		
2		
3		
4		
5		
6		
7		
8		
9		
10		
11		
12		
13		
14		

9. Pick two trials that followed the rule you wrote in step 7 above and fill in Data Table 4 for those trials. To find the change in momentum, take the after momentum – the before momentum.

Data Table 4		
Trial	Cart 1 change in momentum	Cart 2 change in momentum

10. The law of conservation of momentum says that as long as there are no external forces, the momentum in a system must remain unchanged. Use the information in Data Table 4 to explain the law of conservation of momentum.

If we neglect friction, the only forces acting on the cart are internal forces and they

will not affect momentum in the system. The internal forces between the carts

cause impulses on the carts, but they are equal and opposite, so the net change in

momentum for the entire system is 0.

Chapter 7: Linear Momentum and Collisions • Conservation of Momentum

Chapter 7 Lab Finding the Mass of the Glider

Time to Set Up: <1 h
Time in Lab: 1 h
Performance Assessment

Your Task

Using what you know about impulse and conservation of momentum, determine the mass of the glider.

Provide students with an air track, air source, one glider of known mass, and a second glider of unknown mass. You can use two identical gliders and add a large lump of clay to one, or use two different-sized gliders.

Equipment Provided

- air track
- air source
- two gliders

Requirements

- You must design an experiment to solve the problem.
- You may request additional equipment from your instructor.
- You will submit an equipment list and procedure before taking any data.
- You will only get one chance to ask for equipment. Make sure your list is complete.
- Your procedure should be thorough enough that another student in the class could follow your instructions.
- Present your data in tables, if appropriate.
- Show calculations used to solve the problem, if applicable.
- List at least two sources of error. For each, indicate what effect the error would have on your results.

Materials Requested

Students may request photogate timers, stopwatches, digital scales, and
meter sticks.
_____
_____
_____
_____
_____

Procedure Followed

Students will need to conduct a number of trials in which the carts interact.
They can choose to make the carts stick together or bounce off each other.

They should then use the law of conservation of momentum to determine
the unknown mass.

_____

_____

_____

_____

_____

Data Collected

Conclusion

_____

_____

_____

_____

Sources of Error

Possible sources of error include:

• Friction on the air track

• Tracks not being completely level

• Uncertainty in photogate measurements

• Uncertainties in timing with stopwatches

_____

Chapter 8 Lab   Torque and Rotation Exploration

Purpose

In this lab, you will familiarize yourself with the nature of rotational motion and the concepts of torque and moment of inertia.

Materials

Necessary materials will be found at each station.

Discussion

Any force that does not act along a line through the center of mass of an object may cause the object to rotate. The ability of a force to produce rotation is called torque. The torque is defined as the product of a force and the perpendicular distance from the axis about which it rotates. A quantity that represents an object's tendency to resist changes in the object's rotational motion is called the moment of inertia. The greater the moment of inertia, the more difficult it is to change an object's rotational motion. Like inertia for straight-line motion, an object's moment of inertia depends on mass. But unlike translational inertia, the moment of inertia also depends on how the mass is distributed.

Procedure

Station 1: Open the Door

At this station, you will observe the results of applying forces at a variety of points on the door. For the trials described below, apply the same force each time.

Trial 1. Try opening a door by applying force halfway up the door and as far from the hinges as possible.

Trial 2. Apply force as far from the hinges as possible, but higher up on the door.

Trial 3. Apply force at the center of the door.

Trial 4. Apply force at the horizontal center of the door, but at a lower point than in trial 3.

Trial 5. Apply force to the door as close to the hinges as possible.

Time to Set Up: <1 h
Time in Lab: 1 h
Quantitative Lab

Equipment
Any door

In which trial was opening the door easiest? Why?

The door was easiest to open when the force was applied as far from the hinges

as possible. The torque was the greatest when the force was applied here.

In which trial was opening the door the hardest? Why?

The door was hardest to open when the force was applied as close to the

hinges as possible. The torque was the least when the force was applied here.

What one factor seems to determine the ease with which you can cause the door to rotate?

How far from the hinges the force is applied

Station 2: Feel the Torque

Equipment
Meter stick with hook, half-meter stick with two hooks, 500 g mass

Hold the half-meter stick by one end. Place the mass provided at the hook closest to your hand. While keeping your arm stationary, try moving the meter stick up and down using only your wrist.

Now place the mass at the hook farthest from your hand. Once again, try moving the meter stick up and down. Finally, place the mass at the end of the full meter stick and repeat.

In comparing the three trials, was the effort required to lift the mass the same or different? Why do you suppose this is so?

The effort required to lift the mass was greatest when the mass was farthest

from the wrist.

Did the force exerted by gravity on the mass change for each trial?

No, the force of gravity remained constant.

How can you explain any differences between the trials?

The torque depends on both the force and the distance from the pivot

point—in this case the wrist—to the point where the force is applied.

Station 3: Race to the Table Top

Equipment
Two meter sticks, clay

There are two meter sticks at this station. Hold both meter sticks in an upright position with one end of each stick on the table. Release the two meter sticks at the same time.

Which meter stick reached the table first?

Both meter sticks reached the table at the same time.

Describe the motion of the meter sticks as they fell. How did their motions compare?

Both meter sticks accelerated at the same rate.

After attaching a large ball of clay to the upper end of one of the meter sticks, repeat the steps above.

Which meter stick reaches the table first now?

The meter stick without the ball of clay reaches the table first.

You have learned that inertia is a body's resistance to a change in motion. Based on your results, which meter stick, the one with or without the ball of clay, had more inertia?

The meter stick with the ball of clay had more inertia.

Station 4: Soup Can Derby

At this station you will find cans of soup, a ring, a solid disk, and a ramp. Examine the cans. Are the physical properties of the cans the same? That is, do they have the same mass, radius, and height?

Answers will depend on the cans used.

Select two cans of soup to "race" down the ramp. Place both cans at the starting line. Release them at the same time and watch to see which can is the first to reach the bottom of the ramp. Record your description of the cans used in the space provided and circle the winner of each race. Repeat for a different pair of cans.

Race 1: _____ versus _____

Race 2: _____ versus _____

Was the mass or shape of the cans a factor in determining which can won the race? What other factors seem to affect the race results?

Both the mass and the distribution of mass will affect the results.

Now compare the rolling speed of the ring and a solid disk. Relate the behavior of the ring and solid disk to the results of the soup can races.

The ring's moment of inertia is greater than that of the solid disk, because

most of its mass is farther from the center. As a consequence, the solid disk

rotates more easily and will reach the bottom of the ramp sooner. The soup

can with the smallest moment of inertia will reach the bottom first.

Station 5: Clamping Down on Rotation

Hold the meter stick with the two clamps located near the center at the 50 cm mark. Rotate it rapidly in alternating directions. Now do the same with the meter stick with two clamps located near the ends. Which of the two meter stick—clamp systems was easier to rotate? Why do you suppose this is so?

The meter stick with the two clamps near the center at the 50 cm mark will

be easier to rotate, because it has a smaller moment of inertia than the one

with clamps near the ends.

Equipment
Four cans of soup or other food with the same dimensions (make sure that some are solid cream soups and others are liquid soups with noodles); ramp; solid disk and ring, both with the same mass and radius

Equipment
Two meter sticks, four small C clamps

Equipment
Bicycle wheel with handles, rotating stool, two 1 kg masses

Station 6: Spinning Bicycle Wheel

While holding a handle of the bicycle wheel with one hand, set the wheel spinning with the other hand. Now, while holding both handles of the spinning wheel, try to tilt the wheel back and forth. Describe what you feel as you attempt to move the wheel.

The spinning bicycle wheel resists efforts to tilt it and point the axle in a

new direction.

Sit on the stationary rotating stool with the wheel spinning and its axis oriented vertically. What happens when you quickly invert the wheel? Why do you suppose this occurs?

You and the stool will turn. Angular momentum in a closed system is

conserved. When you invert the wheel, you change its angular momentum.

The change in angular momentum of the wheel is compensated for by your

and the stool's opposite change in angular momentum, so that the total

angular momentum remains unchanged.

While sitting on the rotating stool (initially at rest), replace the bicycle wheel with two masses, one in each hand. Have a lab partner set you into a slow rotation. While rotating, move the masses away from your body by stretching out your arms. What happens? Now bring the masses inward toward your chest. What happens now? Explain your observations.

Your rate of rotation will be greater when the masses are close to your body.

A person on a rotating stool has a greater moment of inertia when his or

her arms are outstretched than when the hands are close to the body. The

angular momentum of a closed system must be conserved. Moving the

masses away from the body increases the system's moment of inertia, so

the system's rate of rotation must decrease to compensate.

Chapter 8 Lab   Moment of Inertia

Purpose

In this lab, you will determine the moment of inertia of a metal ring and a uniform, solid metal disk and compare your experimental results with the theoretical values for the moment of inertia of each object, as calculated from their mass and dimensions.

Time to Set Up: <1 h
Time in Lab: 1 h
Quantitative Lab

Discussion

Moment of inertia is a measure of an object's resistance to change in rotational motion. The moment of inertia of an extended rigid object is found by summing the moments of inertia of the particles that make up the object. When this calculation is done for a solid disk, the moment of inertia is found to be $\frac{1}{2}MR^2$, where M is the mass of the disk and R is the disk's radius. For a ring, the moment of inertia is $\frac{1}{2}M(R_1^2 + R_2^2)$, where R_1 and R_2 are the inner and outer radii of the disk, respectively.

The apparatus in this laboratory uses a falling mass to supply the torque that accelerates a turntable and objects placed on it. As the mass accelerates downward, its potential energy (mgh) is transformed into the kinetic energy of the descending mass $\left(\frac{1}{2}mv^2\right)$ and the rotational kinetic energy of the support and the objects on it $\left(\frac{1}{2}I\omega^2\right)$. Applying the conservation of energy to the system,

$$mgh = \frac{1}{2}mv^2 + \frac{1}{2}I\omega^2$$

The distance through which the mass m falls is $h = v_{avg}t = \frac{1}{2}(0 + v_f)t$, where v_f is the final speed of the mass and t is the time of descent of the mass. Solving for v_f, $v_f = 2h/t$. The angular speed of the rotating system equals the speed of the falling mass divided by the radius r of the turntable's axle, that is, $\omega = v/r = 2h/rt$. Substituting these expressions for v and ω into the conservation of energy equation gives

$$mgh = \frac{1}{2}m(2h/t)^2 + \frac{1}{2}I(2h/rt)^2$$

Solving for I,

$$I = mr^2\left(\frac{gt^2}{2h} - 1\right)$$

This equation may be used to determine the experimental values of the moments of inertia of the rotating base, disk, and ring.

Materials

- turntable
- disk
- ring
- string
- two pulleys
- ringstand
- clamp
- mass hanger
- mass set
- Vernier caliper
- stopwatch
- meter stick

Procedure

Part A: Preliminary Measurements

Enter all measurements in Data Table 1.

1. Using a Vernier caliper, measure the diameter of the turntable's axle.

2. Determine the masses of the ring and solid disk.

3. Measure the inner and outer radii of the ring.

4. Measure the radius of the solid disk.

Part B: Overcoming Friction in Turntable and Pulleys

1. Set up the apparatus as shown in the figure.

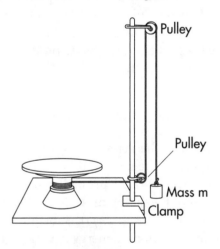

2. To determine the mass required to overcome friction in the turntable's bearings and pulleys, attach the mass hanger to the string. Gradually add mass to the hanger until the hanger descends with a constant speed. This mass will remain on the hanger throughout the rest of these trials. You will repeat this process for each part below.

Part C: Moment of Inertia of Turntable

1. To accelerate the turntable, add an additional 0.05 kg to the hanger.

2. Release the hanger from a height of 1.0 m above the floor and measure the time required for it to reach the floor. Repeat three times. Record the times of descent in Data Table 2.

Part D: Moment of Inertia of the Ring

1. Place the ring on the turntable.

2. Determine the mass required to overcome friction as you did in step 2 of Part B. Record this value in Data Table 3. Keep this mass on the hanger.

3. After adding an additional 0.07 kg to the hanger, repeat step 2 in Part C. Record the times of descent in Data Table 3.

Part E: Moment of Inertia of the Solid Disk

1. Remove the ring and place the solid disk on the turntable.

2. Determine the mass required to overcome friction as you did in step 2 of Part B. Record this value in Data Table 4. Keep this mass on the hanger.

3. After adding an additional 0.07 kg to the hanger, repeat step 2 in Part C. Record the times of descent in Data Table 4.

Data

Data Table 1	
Diameter of turntable axle (m)	
Mass of ring (kg)	
Mass of solid disk (kg)	
Inner radius of ring (m)	
Outer radius of ring (m)	
Radius of solid disk (m)	
Distance mass hanger falls (m)	

Data Table 2: Turntable Alone	
Mass to overcome friction _____ kg (Accelerating mass = 0.05 kg)	
Trial	Time of descent of hanging mass (s)
1	
2	
3	
4	

Average time of descent

_____ s

Data Table 3 Turntable and Ring	
Mass to overcome friction _____ kg (Accelerating mass = 0.07 kg)	
Trial	Time of descent of hanging mass (s)
1	
2	
3	
4	

Average time of descent

_____ s

Data Table 4 Turntable and Solid Disk	
Mass to overcome friction _____ kg (Accelerating mass = 0.07 kg)	
Trial	Time of descent of hanging mass (s)
1	
2	
3	
4	

Average time of descent

_____ s

Analysis

1. Determine the average time of descent for each set of trials.

2. Calculate the experimental moment of inertias of the turntable, turntable and ring, and turntable and disk, using the equation derived in the discussion. Write these values in Table 5.

3. Calculate the experimental moments of inertia of the ring and disk alone by subtracting the moment of inertia of the turntable from the moment of inertia of the turntable and disk or ring. Enter these values in Table 6.

4. Calculate the theoretical moments of inertia for the disk and ring alone. Record these values in Table 6.

5. Calculate the percent error in the experimental values of the moments of inertia, using the theoretical moments of inertia as the accepted values. Record these values in Table 6.

Table 5	
Rotating system	**Experimental moment of inertia (kg m^2)**
Turntable	
Turntable and ring	
Turntable and disk	

Table 6			
Rotating system	**Experimental moment of inertia (kg m^2)**	**Theoretical moment of inertia (kg m^2)**	**% error**
Ring			
Disk			

Conclusions

1. How do the experimental values of the moments of inertia of the ring and disk compare to the theoretical values?

   They should be very similar. _____

   _____

2. List possible sources of error in this laboratory and suggest ways they may be reduced.

   When determining the frictional mass, the turntable may have accelerated. The disk

   and/or ring might be mounted off center. Many of the measurements were difficult

   to make accurately. _____

   _____

Chapter 8 Lab   Balance the Meter Stick

Your Task

Using what you know about static equilibrium and torques, determine where you should place a 50 g mass to balance the meter stick when your teacher gives you a place to put the fulcrum.

Time to Set Up: <1 h
Time in Lab: 1 h
Performance Assessment

Equipment Provided

• meter stick
• meter stick stand
• 50 g mass

Requirements

• You must design an experiment to solve the problem.
• You may request additional equipment from your instructor.
• You will submit an equipment list and procedure before taking any data.
• You will only get one chance to ask for equipment. Make sure your list is complete.
• Your procedure should be thorough enough that another student in the class could follow your instructions.
• Present your data in tables, if appropriate.
• Show calculations used to solve the problem, if applicable.
• List at least two sources of error. For each, indicate what effect the error would have on your results.

Equipment Requested

Students may request a digital scale.
_____
_____
_____
_____
_____
_____

Procedure Followed

Students will need to determine the mass of the meter stick and the
_____
location of its center of mass. The easiest way to determine the latter is
_____

to find where it balances on the stand without any masses attached. You will give each group of students a location to place their fulcrum (30 cm, 40 cm). It is important that you not choose numbers so low or so high that a 50 g mass will not balance the meter stick. This may require some experimentation before the lab.

_____

_____

_____

Data Collected

Conclusion

_____

_____

_____

_____

Sources of Error

Possible sources of error include:

• The mass might not hang directly down.

• The meter stick may not be uniform.

• The 50 g mass might not actually mass 50 g.

Chapter 9: Gravity and Circular Motion • Exploring Circular Motion

Chapter 9 Lab Uniform Circular Motion Exploration

Purpose

In this lab, you will study the motion of objects moving in a circle with constant speed.

Time to Set Up: <1 h
Time in Lab: 1 h
Qualitative Lab

Materials

Necessary materials will be found at each station.

Discussion

Due to inertia, objects tend to travel in a straight line at constant speed. You no doubt can think of many examples of objects that move along a circular path. They may include the rotating turntable in a microwave oven, a car turning a corner, an artificial satellite orbiting the earth in a circular path, or a child on a merry-go-round. According to Newton, in order to deviate from straight-line motion, objects must be acted on by a net external force. This holds true even if the object is moving with constant speed.

Procedure

Station 1: Coin in a Balloon ⚠️ ✋

Insert a dime or penny into an uninflated balloon. After the balloon has been blown up and tied shut, move the balloon rapidly in circles. With a little practice, you should be able to get the coin to orbit on its edge on the inside wall of the balloon. What force keeps the coin moving in circles? Describe the motion of the coin if the balloon were to break.

The inward force supplied by the balloon wall keeps the coin moving along

a circular path. If the balloon were to break, the coin would move off along

a straight line tangent to the circular path.

Equipment
10- or 12-inch balloons, pennies or dimes

It is important to check your class lists for latex allergies.

Station 2: Rotating Candle

Place a candle in a jar. The candle must be shorter than the height of the jar. Place the jar on a turntable and light the candle. Observe the flame as you slowly rotate the turntable. How do you explain the behavior of the flame?

The candle flame leans toward the inside of the turntable for the same

reason that flames move up rather than down. The heated gas of the flame

Equipment
Jar, candle, turntable, matches

Try to attach the jar to the turntable with double-sided tape or other adhesive. Emphasize to students that the turntable should be rotated slowly.

is less dense than the cooler surrounding air, and, having greater inertia than the heated gas, the denser surrounding air moves outward when the turntable is rotated, forcing the candle flame inward.

Station 3: Constant-Velocity Car on a String

Equipment
Constant-velocity car, string

Attach a string, approximately 0.4 m long, to the center of a constant-velocity car. Place the car on a table top and extend the string. While holding onto the free end of the string, set the car in motion. Describe the motion of the car. Now release the string and observe the motion of the car. Explain reasons for any changes you observe in the car's motion.

The car will travel in a circle as long as the student holds on to the cord.

When the cord is released, the car will move off along a straight line. This

occurs because an inward force is required to maintain circular motion.

Station 4: Conical Pendulum

Equipment
0.5 kg mass, 0.5 m cord,
spring scale

Use a 0.5 m cord to attach a 0.5 kg mass to a spring scale. Suspend the mass by the cord and read the scale. Now move the scale so that the hanging mass moves in a circle with the string tracing out a cone. Observe the scale reading while the mass is moving. Compare the scale reading obtained while the mass is at rest to the reading produced when the mass is moving in a circle. Explain any differences you observe.

The scale reading is greater when the mass is moving in a circle. The

stationary mass is subject to the downward force of gravity only. This is

countered by the tension in the cord. When the mass is moving, the tension

now must provide both the vertical force to balance the force of gravity and

the horizontal force needed to keep the mass moving in a horizontal circular

orbit. Therefore, the scale reading must be greater.

Station 5: Bucket of Water Trick ⚠

Equipment
Bucket, water

Swing the plastic bucket containing water in a vertical circle. Describe the behavior of the water as the bucket moves in a circle. Explain what would happen to the water if the bucket were to stop directly over your head.

This activity requires space
and should preferably be done
outside, with the students
standing at least 10 m from the
swinging bucket.

As the bucket of water is swung, it experiences a net force toward the center.

This force is provided by the person swinging the bucket. The unbalanced

force creates an acceleration toward the center. As the bucket moves faster, a

greater force is required to keep the bucket moving along the circular path.

This results in a greater inward acceleration. When the bucket is overhead, the

bucket is accelerating toward the center of the motion at a rate greater than

the acceleration due to gravity. As a result, the water stays inside the bucket.

As you rotated the bucket in the vertical circle, where did the bucket feel heaviest? Lightest? Explain your observations.

At the top of its path, the bucket feels lighter than normal because gravity

is providing a portion of the net inward force required to maintain circular

motion. At the bottom, the bucket feels heavier than normal because your

arm must now not only oppose the gravitational force (the bucket's weight)

but also provide the net inward force that keeps it moving in a circle.

Station 6: Flying Toy

Turn the toy on. Set the toy in motion by giving it a push. Observe the toy once it achieves a stable circular motion. Draw a force diagram for the toy when it is at the 3 o'clock position when you look at it from below.

If the string were to break, what path would the plane follow?

The toy would go horizontally tangent to the circle at the point where the

string broke, but also vertically downward due to gravity. So this would

result in a parabolic path.

If the batteries were to wear down, how would the motion of the toy change?

The velocity of the toy would decrease. It would move in a circle with a

smaller radius.

Station 7: Scorcher Chamber

Place the car, with spring wound, on the wall and near the bottom of the bucket. With the car positioned parallel to the bottom of the bucket, launch the car by giving it a push.

Describe the motion of the car once it is released.

_____

_____

Suggest an explanation for the car's motion.

The car should "stick" to the wall of the bucket. The centripetal force

provided by the bucket acts normally on the car. This normal force gives

rise to an upward-directed frictional force that counteracts the downward

gravitational force, keeping the car from falling.

Equipment

Flying toy, such as a pig or plane that attaches to the ceiling and moves in a circular path

The flying toy used in this activity is available in the form of an airplane, pig, and cow from suppliers of science education apparatus.

Equipment

Bucket, spring-wound toy car

Equipment
Bubble level

Station 8: Bubble Level Accelerometer

Hold the bubble level so that it is parallel to the floor and the bubble is in the center of the glass tube. Now accelerate the level to the right and then slow down. Notice how the bubble responds when you speed up and when you slow down. Does the bubble move in the direction of the acceleration or in the opposite direction? Now hold the level so that is perpendicular to your body. Have your lab partner observe the movement of the bubble as you spin in a circle. How does the bubble respond to your spinning? Based on what you know about the response of the bubble to acceleration, do objects moving in a circle experience an acceleration? If so, describe the direction of the acceleration.

The bubble moves in the direction of the acceleration. The bubble moves

inward when the level is spun in a circle. Thus, objects moving in a circle

must experience an acceleration toward the center of the circle.

Chapter 9 Lab   Centripetal Force on a Pendulum

Purpose

In this lab, you will investigate the centripetal force acting on a pendulum bob. A force sensor will be used to measure the centripetal force and a photogate to measure the bob's velocity at the lowest point in the pendulum's swing. The measured force will be compared to the calculated force obtained from the pendulum's speed, mass, and length.

Discussion

To maintain circular motion, an object must be acted on by a net centripetal force. In the case of a pendulum, the tension in the cord supplies the centripetal force. At the lowest point in a pendulum's swing, the net force on the bob is equal to the vector sum of the tension T in the string and the force of gravity.

Materials

- force sensor
- photogate and timer
- interface
- pendulum bob
- cord

- Vernier caliper
- triple beam balance
- meter stick
- ringstand
- rods and clamps

Time to Set Up: <1 h
Time in Lab: 1 h
Quantitative Lab

Procedure

1. Find the mass of the pendulum bob and record it in Data Table 1.

2. Use the Vernier caliper to measure the width of the pendulum bob and enter the value in Data Table 1.

3. Set up the apparatus as shown in Figure 1.

Figure 1

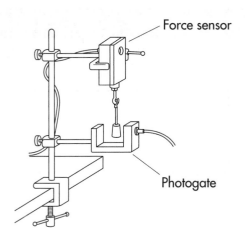

Force sensor

Photogate

4. Connect the timer and force sensor to the interface.

5. Zero the force probe.

6. Using a length of cord, attach the bob to the force sensor. While the length of the cord chosen is not critical, you may wish to begin by using a length of approximately 0.5 m.

7. Position the photogate so that the center of the pendulum bob blocks the photogate beam when the bob is hanging freely. Once the bob has been suspended from the force probe, the distance between the cord's point of attachment to the force sensor and the center of the bob should be measured carefully and recorded as the radius R of the pendulum's circular path in Data Table 1.

8. Use the force sensor to measure the weight of the freely hanging bob. Enter the weight in Data Table 1.

9. Displace the bob through an angle of approximately 25°. After activating the timer, release the bob. Have someone catch the bob on the other side of its swing.

10. The timer displays the time it took for the bob to pass through the photogate. Record this time as Δt in Data Table 2.

11. At the bottom of the swing, the tension in the cord is the greatest and is equal to the weight of the bob plus the centripetal force required to keep the bob moving in a circle. Use the interface tools to determine the maximum force F_{max} on the bob. Record this force in Data Table 2.

12. Repeat steps 9 through 11 four more times and record in Data Table 2.

You may wish to have students experiment with pendulum bobs having different masses, different lengths of cord, or different initial displacements.

Data

Data Table 1	
Mass of pendulum bob (kg)	
Width of pendulum bob (m)	
Radius R (m)	
Weight of bob (N)	

Data Table 2		
Trial	Δt (s)	F_{Max} (N)
1		
2		
3		
4		
5		

Table 3		
Trial	Velocity (m/s)	F_c calculated (N)
1		
2		
3		
4		
5		

Table 4	
Trial	F_c measured (N)
1	
2	
3	
4	
5	

Analysis

1. Calculate the speed of the pendulum bob at the lowest point of the pendulum's swing for each trial and record this in Table 3.

2. Calculate the centripetal force F_c for each trial from the mass of the pendulum bob m, radius of bob's circular path R, and the calculated speed of the pendulum bob v, and enter in Table 3.

3. Draw a force diagram showing the forces acting on the moving pendulum bob at its lowest point.

4. Write an equation for the centripetal force on the bob at the lowest point in its motion in terms of the forces identified in step 3. Use this equation to determine the centripetal force that acted on the bob for each of your five trials and record in Table 4.

Conclusions

1. How should the calculated and measured values for the two centripetal forces for each trial compare? Looking at your data, did you find this to be true?

2. What are the possible reasons for any discrepancies between the two values?

Chapter 9: Gravity and Circular Motion • Circular Motion

Chapter 9 Lab   Give Me an "r"

Your Task

Using what you know about circular motion, determine the maximum radius at which the penny will remain in a circular path on the turntable. Students will be given the rotation speed at which the penny must remain stationary.

Equipment Provided

- turntable
- penny
- ruler

Requirements

- You must design an experiment to solve the problem.
- You may request additional equipment from your instructor.
- You will submit an equipment list and procedure before taking any data.
- You will only get one chance to ask for equipment. Make sure your list is complete.
- Your procedure should be thorough enough that another student in the class could follow your instructions.
- Present your data in tables, if appropriate.
- Show calculations used to solve the problem, if applicable.
- List at least two sources of error. For each, indicate what effect the error would have on your results.

Materials Requested

Students may request a spring scale, protractor, digital scale, and stopwatch.

_____

_____

_____

_____

_____

Time to Set Up: <1 h
Time in Lab: 1 h
Performance Assessment

If using a turntable, assign different speeds (33⅓, 45, 78) to different groups.

Procedure Followed

Students will need to determine the coefficient of friction between the
turntable and the penny. The easiest way to do this is to tilt the turntable
and determine the angle at which the penny just begins to slide down.
They might try to use a spring scale, but this method will be very inaccurate.
Once they know the coefficient of friction, they can determine the radius
using the fact that the centripetal force will be equivalent to the force of
friction.

_____

_____

_____

Data Collected

Conclusion

_____

_____

_____

_____

Sources of Error

Possible sources of error include:

• Finding the coefficient of friction can be quite tricky.

• They may have tilted the turntable at too large an angle.

• The rotating turntable may not be 100% level.

• The turntable might not maintain a constant speed, and its speed may not
  be exactly 33⅓ (or 45 or 78) rpm.

Chapter 10: Temperature and Heat • Exploring Temperature and Heat

Chapter 10 Lab   Temperature and Heat Exploration

Purpose

In this lab, you will investigate the physics of temperature and heat and some of the interesting behavior associated with these quantities.

Materials

Necessary materials will be found at each station.

Discussion

Although temperature and heat are related, they are not the same. Temperature is defined as the average kinetic energy of molecules that make up an object. When two objects with different temperatures are brought into contact, energy will flow from the object with higher temperature to the object with the lower temperature. The energy that is transferred from one object to another because of a difference in temperature is called heat. Forms of thermal energy exchange include conduction, convection, and radiation. Changes in the internal energy of an object or substance may result in a change of state or in contraction or expansion.

Procedure

Station 1: Convection Currents

Place a lighted candle approximately 25 cm in front of a white screen. With the room lights off, shine a bright light toward the candle and the screen. Describe what you see on the screen above the candle's shadow.

Students should witness rising shadow patterns on the screen.

_____

What do you think produces what you see on the screen?

These patterns are produced by the refraction of light as it passes through

the convection currents rising above the candle's flame.

_____

Station 2: Radiation—Visible and Invisible

Bring the light bulb near the radiometer. Turn on the light and observe the motion of the vanes inside the radiometer. What effect does the light have on the vanes?

Light will cause the vanes to rotate.

_____

Time to Set Up: <1 h
Time in Lab: 1 h
Qualitative Lab

Equipment
Candle, matches, flashlight, or other light source; white paper or cardboard

A point source of light works best. However, a standard flashlight may be used. A dark environment is necessary if convection currents are to be observed. A lava lamp also may be used to demonstrate convection.

Equipment
Radiometer, light bulb, hair dryer

Why do you think this is so?

The dark sides of the vanes become warmer than the light sides. Faster

moving molecules near the black surface produce a net force on the vanes.

Now turn off the light and direct an operating hair dryer toward the radiometer. What do you observe now?

The vanes turn.

What is causing the vanes to turn this time?

Infrared radiation from the hair dryer's heating element has the same effect

on the vanes as visible light.

Station 3: The Drinking Bird

Equipment
Drinking bird, glass of water

Observe the motion of the drinking bird. What function does the water play in the operation of the drinking bird?

Evaporating water cools the head and lowers vapor pressure inside it.

The toy is safe as long as it is not broken. It contains a hazardous fluid, which, when released, evaporates quickly. This fluid can irritate the skin and the lungs if inhaled. Good ventilation should be provided after a spill to dilute and disperse the vapor.

Will the bird continue to bob up and down if the glass of water is removed? If so, for how long?

The bird will continue until the head is dry.

Do you think the relative humidity of the surrounding air affects the rate of dipping of the bird? Explain your reasoning.

High humidity reduces rate of evaporation and rate of bobbing.

Station 4: The Heat Capacity of Water

Equipment
Water-filled balloon, candle, matches

Observe what happens when you hold the water-filled balloon in the candle flame. Does the balloon burst? Explain your observations.

The balloon does not burst. Even though the flame from the candle can easily

melt or burn rubber, heat is readily dissipated into the water and away from the

wall of the balloon so that the rubber does not heat up enough to melt or burn.

What would happen if you were to hold a match beneath an air-filled balloon (DO NOT TRY THIS!).

It would burst because air has a lower heat capacity than water.

Station 5: Boiling with Body Heat

Equipment
Hand boiler

Hand boilers are available from many suppliers of science education equipment. The fluid in the hand boiler is similar to that found in the drinking bird. Good ventilation should be provided if the device is broken.

Wrap your hand around the hand boiler. Describe the behavior of the colored liquid inside the device as you hold it in your hand. Explain your observations.

The liquid used in the hand boiler has a boiling point just above room

temperature. Heat from your hand causes the liquid to boil, which in turn

makes the liquid evaporate, turning it to gas. The expanding gas pushes the
liquid upward.

Station 6: Ice Cube Lifter

Float an ice cube in a full cup of cold water. Lay the center of the
string on the ice cube and sprinkle salt on the ice and the string. After
approximately 1 minute, observe what happens when you lift both ends
of the string. What must have happened to the ice that was initially
beneath the string after the salt was sprinkled on the ice and string?
The ice must have melted and then refrozen.

What do you think salt does to the melting point of ice?
The salt lowers the melting point of ice.

Where else is this principle of lowering the melting point of ice applied
in daily life?
Salt is frequently used to melt ice on sidewalks and roads and to lower the

freezing temperature in ice cream makers.

Equipment
Ice cube, cup of cold water,
string, salt

Station 7: Your Sense of Temperature

Place one hand on a piece of carpeting and the other on a piece of floor
tile. Which feels warmer?
The carpet will feel warmer.

Use the thermometer to measure the temperatures of the carpet and
floor tile. How do the actual temperatures of these objects compare?
The temperatures are the same.

Is your sense of warm and cold consistent with the temperature
measured with the thermometer? Why do you suppose this is so?
No, the way we sense temperature is not consistent with the temperature

measured by the thermometer. The tile has a higher thermal conductivity

and carries heat away from the hand more rapidly.

Equipment
Piece of carpet, floor tile, liquid
crystal or infrared thermometer

You may wish to try a variety of
materials, such as metal, Styrofoam, glass, and plastic.

Station 8: Temperature-Sensitive Tapes

Cut 10-cm-long strips of masking tape and transparent tape. Place
the sticky sides of the two pieces of tape together. Use scissors to trim
the combined strips so that the strips match up exactly. Observe what
happens when you hold one end of the taped pair vertically about 10 cm
above an incandescent light bulb. (Don't let the tape touch the bulb.)
Describe what you see.
The tape pair bends to one side.

Equipment
Masking tape, transparent tape

Why do you think this occurs?

When the tape pair is heated, the difference in the expansion coefficients of the two tapes makes the pair bend.

How might a device such as this be used to control a furnace or air conditioner?

Bimetallic strips, made of two metals, are used in thermostats.

Chapter 10 Lab   Linear Expansion

Purpose

In this lab, you will determine the coefficient of linear expansion for two metals and compare the results to accepted values.

Time to Set Up: <1 h
Time in Lab: 1 h
Quantitative Lab

Discussion

In general, matter expands when it is heated. In the case of a solid, the change in length depends on three factors: the change in temperature, the original length of the solid, and the composition of the solid. The relationship between these factors is expressed by the equation $\Delta L = \alpha L_i \Delta T$, where ΔL is the change in length, L_i is the initial length, ΔT is the change in temperature of the material, and α is the coefficient of linear expansion, a constant that depends on the material. In this experiment, the coefficients of linear expansion of aluminum and copper will be determined.

(1)

Materials

- linear expansion apparatus with dial gauge
- steam generator
- rubber hose
- catch basin

- thermometer
- aluminum and copper rods
- thermal laboratory gloves or pot holders

Procedure

1. The linear expansion apparatus will be set up as shown in Figure 1.

Figure 1

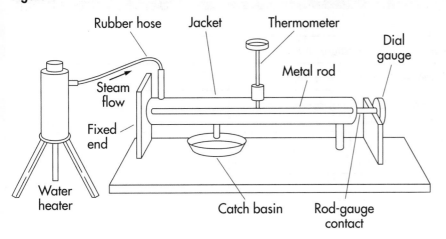

There are several types of expansion apparatuses. Some gauges require that they be backed off during expansion and later be brought back into contact with the fully expanded rod. Make certain the students know how to use the gauge for your apparatus. Due to time constraints, you may wish to assign each lab group only one type of metal rod with which to experiment, and then have the groups compare results.

Students should wear goggles throughout the experiment. Those handling the steam generator, expansion apparatus, and metal rods should wear thermal gloves.

The precision of measurement depends on the apparatus.

If you have multiple sections, you will need to cool the rods between classes.

2. After selecting one of the two metal rods, use a meter stick to measure its initial length to the nearest millimeter. Record this length in Data Table 1.

3. Measure the room temperature to the nearest 0.1°. Record this temperature as the initial temperature in Data Table 1.

4. Insert the metal rod into the apparatus jacket.

5. Adjust the dial gauge until the gauge's contact just touches the rod. Read the gauge and record its value as the initial gauge reading in Data Table 1.

6. Insert the thermometer into the hole in the center of the apparatus. Gently push the thermometer until it comes in contact with the rod.

7. Bring the water to a boil.

8. Allow steam to pass through the jacket until the thermometer reading remains constant. Record this reading as the final temperature in Data Table 1. Also, note and record the final gauge reading.

9. Wearing thermal gloves, remove the hose from the apparatus. Repeat steps 2 through 9 using the other rod.

Data

Data Table 1		
	Aluminum	**Copper**
Initial length of rod (m)		
Initial temperature of rod (°C)		
Final temperature of rod (°C)		
Initial gauge reading (m)		
Final gauge reading (m)		

Table 2		
	Aluminum	**Copper**
Change in temperature of rod (°C)		
Change in length of rod (m)		
Experimental value of coefficient of linear expansion (/°C)		
Accepted value of coefficient of linear expansion (/°C)		
Percent error		

Analysis

1. Calculate the change in temperature of each rod and enter in Table 2.

2. Calculate the change in length of each rod and enter in Table 2.

3. Calculate the coefficient of linear expansion for each rod, using the relationship $\Delta L = \alpha L_i \Delta T$. Enter your answers in Table 2.

4. Use your text to find the accepted coefficients of linear expansion for the two metals. Enter these values in Table 2.

5. Calculate the percent error in experimental values of the coefficients of linear expansion. Enter these values in Table 2.

Conclusions

1. What are the possible reasons for any discrepancies between the experimental and accepted values for the coefficients of linear expansion?

   Discrepancies may exist due to errors in measuring the length of the rods and reading

   the gauge and thermometer. Error may have been introduced if the temperature of

   the rod was not uniform.

2. Using the equation for linear expansion, show why the units for the coefficient of expansion are /°C.

   Since $\alpha = \Delta L / L \Delta T$, the units are m/(m °C) or /°C.

3. How would the measured coefficient of linear expansion be affected if all lengths were measured in inches?

   The coefficient is a ratio of the lengths, so any unit is appropriate for measuring the

   length.

Chapter 10: Temperature and Heat • Heat of Fusion and Specific Heat

Chapter 10 Lab   Easy on the Ice

Your Task

You will be given a container of water and some ice at 0°C. You will add the ice to the water. You must then determine the mass of the ice that was added to the water.

Equipment Provided

- water
- ice

Requirements

- You must design an experiment to solve the problem.
- You may request additional equipment from your instructor.
- You will submit an equipment list and procedure before taking any data.
- You will only get one chance to ask for equipment. Make sure your list is complete.
- Your procedure should be thorough enough that another student in the class could follow your instructions.
- Present your data in tables, if appropriate.
- Show calculations used to solve the problem, if applicable.
- List at least two sources of error. For each, indicate what effect the error would have on your results.

Materials Requested

Students may ask for the following equipment: calorimeter or Styrofoam cup,

thermometer, digital scale, graduated cylinder. _____

_____

_____

_____

_____

Procedure Followed

Students should record the temperature and mass of the water before they

add the ice. They should also measure the temperature after the ice was

added. You should discourage students from massing the ice/water mixture,

Time to Set Up: <1 h
Time in Lab: 1 h
Performance Assessment

Provide students with water and ice. Make sure the ice is at 0°C. You might want to allow them time to brainstorm before giving them the ice. If desired, record the mass of the ice before you give it to the students. Use these data to check the accuracy of their results.

as this makes the problem trivial. Students can find the mass of the ice using the fact that the energy is conserved in the system. It is important for the students to remember that not only does the ice melt, but the temperature of the resulting water is also changed.

_____

_____

_____

Data Collected

Conclusion

_____

_____

_____

_____

Sources of Error

Possible sources of error include:

• Heat loss to the surrounding environment.

• The original temperature of the ice.

• Some of the ice melts before it's put into the water.

There are no labs for Chapter 11.

There are no labs for Chapter 11.

Chapter 12: Gases, Liquids, and Solids • Exploring Fluids

Chapter 12 Lab   Exploration

Purpose

In this lab, you will familiarize yourself with the ways gases and liquids behave when at rest and while in motion.

Time to Set Up: <1 h
Time in Lab: 1 h
Qualitative Lab

Materials

Necessary materials will be found at each station.

Discussion

A fluid is a substance that has no fixed shape and yields easily to external pressure. Liquids and gases are both fluids. Unlike solids, fluids flow and change shape easily. Fluids play an important role in our daily lives, for, among other things, they are central to breathing, drinking, flying, and swimming. The study of fluids may be divided into two main areas: fluid statics and fluid dynamics. As the names suggest, fluid statics deals with fluids at rest, while fluid dynamics is concerned with the movement of fluids. In this activity you will examine phenomena illustrating aspects of both fluid statics and fluid dynamics.

Procedure

Station 1: Diet or Regular? 🔦

Dry the cans of soda and mass them.

Diet _____ g Regular _____ g

Equipment
A can of diet soda and a can of regular soda, a large beaker or bucket, water

Place the cans in the water. What do you observe?

The diet soda will float, while the regular soda sinks.

Explain your observations.

The diet soda has less mass than the regular soda. Both have the same

volume. Therefore, the density of the diet soda is less than the density of

the regular soda.

Station 2: Floaters or Sinkers?

Copy this chart in your lab notebook.

Equipment
A large tub or bucket full of water, miscellaneous objects. It is best to have both objects that will sink and objects that will float on the water.

Object	Prediction (S or F)	Actual (S or F)

For each item, predict whether it will sink or float in the water.

Test them out and fill in the "actual" column on the chart.

Why did some things sink and others float?

If an object has a density less than the liquid you are placing it in, it will

float.

Equipment
Tub of water, clay

Station 3: Whatever Floats Your Boat
Place the lump of clay in the water. Note what happens.

The clay will sink.

Is there a way you can make the clay float? Try it out! Explain what method you used.

Yes, if the clay is placed in a boat that displaces a sufficient volume of water,

the buoyant force on the boat will be larger than the combined weight of

the clay and the boat. This will cause the boat to float.

Equipment
Three balloons filled with different volumes of helium, a force probe and computer or interface, and string. Tie the balloons to an anchor so they don't ascend to the ceiling.

Station 4: Floaters
Compare the helium balloons. How are they different?

The balloons have different volumes.

Use the force probe to determine the upward force each balloon exerts.

Balloon	Upward force (N)

Explain any differences in the values you entered in the table.

The balloon with the largest volume displaces the largest volume of air and

thus experiences the largest buoyant force.

Equipment
Paper and two books

Station 5: Blow under the Paper
Place two books side by side but separated on the table. Place a sheet of paper over the books to create a tunnel with a paper "roof." What do you think will happen when you blow air through the tunnel?

Blow in the tunnel created between the table and the paper. Describe what happens.

The paper should bow down into the tunnel space.

Explain your results.

The moving air creates a low-pressure region inside the tunnel. There is thus a pressure difference between the air above the tunnel and the air in the tunnel. The higher pressure above the tunnel pushes the paper downward.

Station 6: Two Cans

At this station, two empty soda cans are hanging close to each other. What do you think will happen if you blow between the cans?

Equipment
Two ringstands, a horizontal bar, two right-angle clamps, two empty soda cans, string

Assembly
Secure the horizontal bar between the ringstands. Use the string to attach the cans so that they hang freely from the horizontal bar.

Try it! Explain your results.

When you blow between the cans, a low-pressure region is created between the cans. The higher pressure on the outside of the cans pushes them into each other.

Station 7: Ping-Pong Ball Trick

Clean the funnel using the alcohol wipe. Hold the ping-pong ball inside the funnel. Turn the funnel sideways, like a trumpet, and blow through it. What happens to the ball?

The ball should remain inside the funnel, even though you are blowing the air out of the funnel.

Equipment
Alcohol wipes, small funnel, ping-pong ball

Can you turn the funnel upside down? Explain your observations.

Yes, you can hold the funnel upside down and the ball will remain in the funnel while you are blowing through it. The movement of the air creates a low-pressure region around the ball. The pressure on the outside of the funnel is greater than the pressure inside it, and thus the ball does not fall.

Station 8: Changing the Nozzle

Turn on the water and watch the water flow into the sink. Change the area of the nozzle by placing your finger over the end of the hose. How does this affect the water flow? Explain your observations.

When you place your finger over the nozzle, you reduce the area and the velocity of the water increases.

Equipment
Faucet with attached hose or tubing

Chapter 12: Gases, Liquids, and Solids • Archimedes' Principle

Chapter 12 Lab   Archimedes' Principle

Purpose

In this lab, you will discover the relationship between buoyant force, volume, and weight of water displaced.

Time to Set Up: <1 h
Time in Lab: 1 h
Quantitative Lab

Discussion

A fluid surrounding an object exerts a buoyant force in the upward direction. This is because pressure increases with depth, and hence the upward force on an immersed object is greater than the downward force. The Greek scientist and mathematician Archimedes discovered that an object partially or fully immersed in a fluid is buoyed up by a force equal to the weight of the fluid displaced by the object. This became known as Archimedes' principle. Legend has it that Archimedes was so moved by his discovery that he jumped out of the bath and ran naked down the street, shouting "Eureka, Eureka!" (I've found it!).

Archimedes' principle applies to objects of all densities. According to Archimedes' principle, if an object's density is greater than that of the fluid, the buoyant force will be less than the object's weight and the object will sink. Likewise, if the object's density is less than that of the fluid, the object will float.

Materials

- one set of density blocks
- graduated cylinder
- digital scale
- tub of water
- force probe
- computer interface
- overflow can
- ruler
- beaker
- washers
- paper towels

Density blocks are available from many sources. It is best to use a set that has objects of different volumes. Spring scales may be used, but force probes are preferable because the difference between the weight of an object in air and its weight in water might be small.

Procedure 🔧

Part A: Floaters and Sinkers

1. Use the scale to determine the mass of each object. Record these answers in Data Table 1.

2. Determine the volume of each object. There are several ways to do this. Record your volumes in Data Table 1.

3. Predict which objects will sink and which will float. Record your predictions in Data Table 2.

Students can calculate the volume using the blocks' dimensions or using the water displacement method.

4. Place each of these objects in water. As you place each item in the water, note whether it sinks or floats. Enter these results in Data Table 2.

Part B: ONLY for Sinkers

Use the same items as in Part A, but use only the objects that SANK in the water for this part of the lab.

1. Use the force probe to weigh the objects in the air. You may need to tie a string to the object to do this. Enter your data in Data Table 3.

2. Use the force probe to weigh the objects while they are entirely submerged in water. Enter your data in Data Table 3.

3. Place a beaker under the spout from the overflow can to catch any water that comes out of the spout. Fill an overflow can with water and wait until it no longer drips into the beaker. Empty the beaker and place it under the spout again. Gently place the object into the overflow can. Make certain that the beaker catches the displaced water.

Students need to find the mass of just the water.

4. Use a scale to determine the mass of the displaced water. Record these data in Data Table 3.

Part C: ONLY for Floaters

Use the same items as in Part A, but use only the objects that FLOATED in the water for this part of the lab.

1. Place the object so that it floats on the water.

Students must be careful when placing washers so that the objects don't tip.

2. Gently add washers to the top of the object, one at a time, until the object sinks.

3. Mass the washers that sank the object. Enter your data in Data Table 4.

4. Use the overflow can and the method outlined in Part B to determine the volume of your object. You may need to gently push your object under the water to obtain its complete volume.

5. Use a graduated cylinder and determine the volume of the displaced water. Enter your data in Data Table 4.

Data Table 1			
Object	Mass (kg)	Volume (m^3)	Density (kg/m^3)

Data Table 2		
Object	Predicted (sink or float?)	Experimental (sink or float?)

Data Table 3			
Object	Weight in air (N)	Weight in water (N)	Mass of displaced water (kg)

Data Table 4		
Object	Mass of washers to sink (kg)	Mass of water displaced (kg)

Analysis and Conclusions

Part A

1. Determine the density of each object using density = mass/volume. Enter your values in Table 5.

2. Ask your teacher for the accepted density for each of the objects. Use these values and the ones you calculated in Data Table 1 to determine your percent error.

Your density blocks should come with a list of the accepted densities.

Table 5			
Object	Calculated density	Accepted density	% error

3. The density of water is 1000 kg/m³. Look at the densities of the objects that floated or sank—what determines whether an object will sink or float?

If an object's density is less than the density of water, it will float. If it is

more than the density of water, the object will sink.

4. Based on your answer to step 3 above, which of the objects would float in oil (density = 900 kg/m³)?

Answers will depend on the objects used. In general, anything with a

density less than 900 kg/m³ will float in oil.

Part B

1. Draw a force diagram for an object while it is suspended by the string in the water.

2. Using the weight in air and the weight in water, determine the buoyant force that acted on each object. Enter your values in Table 6.

3. Determine the weight of the displaced water using $F_g = mg$. Enter your values in Table 6.

4. Archimedes' principle says that the buoyant force is equal to the weight of the water displaced. Do your data support this result? Explain.

Data should be close enough that students can see that the buoyant

force does equal the weight of the water displaced.

Table 6		
Object	Buoyant force (N)	Weight of displaced water (N)

Part C

1. Draw a force diagram for an object when it is floating.

2. Using $F_b = \rho g V$, determine the maximum buoyant force each object would experience if totally submerged. Water has a density of 1000 kg/m³. Enter these values in Table 7.

3. Determine the weight of the object AND extra mass when it sank.

4. What relationship do you see between the maximum buoyant force and the total weight (object + washers)? Explain.

These values should be equivalent. When an object floats, the buoyant

force must equal the weight of the entire object.

Table 7		
Object	Maximum F_b (N)	Total weight (N)

Chapter 12: Gases, Liquids, and Solids • Bernoulli's Equation

Chapter 12 Lab   Finding the Range

Your Task

There is a hole in the water bottle. The water will stream out the hole and land on the table top below. You must predict where the water stream will hit and place an "X" on the paper towel at that location.

Equipment Provided

• water bottle with hole
• water

Requirements

• You must design an experiment to solve the problem.
• You may request additional equipment from your instructor.
• You will submit an equipment list and procedure before taking any data.
• You will only get one chance to ask for equipment. Make sure your list is complete.
• Your procedure should be thorough enough that another student in the class could follow your instructions.
• Present your data in tables, if appropriate.
• Show calculations used to solve the problem, if applicable.
• List at least two sources of error. For each, indicate the effect the error would have on your results.

Materials Requested

Students may request meter sticks or rulers.

_____

_____

_____

_____

_____

Procedure Followed

Students should use Bernoulli's equation to determine the velocity of the

water as it exits the hole. From this they can apply the equations used to

Time to Set Up: <1 h
Time in Lab: 1 h
Performance Assessment

Use a nail to puncture a hole in the water bottle. Make certain that the water exits the bottle horizontally.

describe the motion of a projectile to determine the range of the water
stream.

_____

_____

_____

_____

_____

_____

Data Collected

Conclusion

_____

_____

_____

_____

Sources of Error

Possible sources of error include:

• The water level is constantly changing.

• Bernoulli's equation assumes that the liquid has no viscosity.

• The water might not have exited the hole exactly horizontally.

Chapter 13 Lab   Exploring Waves on a Coiled Spring

Purpose

In this lab, you will explore the properties of pulses and waves traveling on a coiled spring.

Time to Set Up: <1 h
Time in Lab: 1 h
Qualitative Lab

Materials

- coiled spring (Slinky)
- masking tape
- string

Discussion

A mechanical pulse, or wave, is a disturbance that travels through some material medium transporting energy, but not matter. There are essentially two types of mechanical waves: transverse and longitudinal. We will investigate both types. In the case of transverse waves, particles in the medium move perpendicular to the direction of wave propagation. With longitudinal waves, the particles in a medium vibrate parallel to the direction of propagation.

Procedure

1. With your lab partner's help, stretch the spring to a length of 5 to 8 m on a smooth horizontal surface. To prevent possible tangling, be careful not to let go of the spring. Attach small pieces of masking tape at equal intervals along the coiled spring.

2. Produce a pulse by quickly moving one end of the spring to the side and back again. Describe the shape of the spring with the pulse on it.

The pulse should appear hump-shaped.

Does the spring remain permanently altered by the pulse's brief presence, or does it return to its original state?

The spring does not remain permanently altered.

Describe the motion of the pieces of masking tape when the pulse reaches them.

Each piece of tape moves to the side and then back as the pulse reaches it.

Do the pieces of tape move parallel or perpendicular to the direction of motion of the pulse?

The pieces of tape move perpendicular to the direction of motion of the pulse.

Is this pulse transverse or longitudinal?

Because the tape moves perpendicular to the motion of the pulse, the pulse is transverse.

3. Create a pulse and describe any changes in the shape and amplitude (height) of the pulse as it travels down and back up the spring. What do you think causes these changes?

The shape remains essentially the same, but the amplitude of the pulse decreases due to friction.

4. Produce two pulses in rapid succession. The second pulse should have considerably larger amplitude than the first. Does the distance between the pulses change as they travel along the spring?

The distance between the two pulses remains the same.

What does this indicate about the relationship between amplitude and the speed of the pulse?

The amplitude does not affect the speed of the pulse.

5. Send another pulse down the spring and observe what happens when it reaches your partner's hand. How do the shape and amplitude of the reflected pulse compare to those of the incoming pulse?

The reflected pulse has the same shape and amplitude as the incoming pulse.

Does the reflected pulse come back on the same side or the opposite side of the spring?

The reflected pulse comes back on the opposite side of the spring.

6. Gather up several coils of the spring. This will increase the tension in the spring without altering its length. Send a pulse down the spring. How does increasing the tension seem to affect the speed of the pulse?

Increasing the tension increases the speed of the pulse.

7. You have seen how a pulse reflects from a fixed end in step 5 above. To simulate reflection from a free end, tie approximately 3 m of string to one end of the spring. While your partner holds the string, move back a bit to establish tension in the spring, and generate a

transverse pulse by shaking the end of the spring. Do you observe a reflected pulse?

Yes, there should still be a reflected pulse.

If so, does it return on the same or the opposite side of the spring?

The reflected pulse is now on the same side as the incoming pulse.

8. Remove the string from the Slinky. With your partner's help, simultaneously send two pulses, one from each end, down the spring. The pulses should be on the same side of the spring. What happens when the pulses meet? Do they bounce off or pass through each other?

The pulses pass through each other.

One way to answer this question is to produce two pulses of noticeably different amplitudes. This will enable you to keep track of the pulses before and after they meet. Study the spring's amplitude very carefully at the instant the pulses meet. Describe the amplitude of the spring at that instant. Is it greater than, less than, or the same as that of the individual pulses?

When the pulses meet, the amplitude of the spring is greater than that

of either of the individual pulses.

9. With your partner's help, simultaneously send pulses of equal amplitude from each end and on opposite sides of the spring. Describe the shape of the spring when the two pulses meet.

If the pulses are of equal amplitude, the spring should have no amplitude

when the pulses meet.

10. Send a train of waves down the spring by continuously moving your hand back and forth with a constant frequency. How does the frequency of the waves passing any point on the spring compare to the frequency of your hand movement?

The frequency of the waves passing any point on the spring equals the

frequency of hand movement.

11. Gather up 10 coils at one end of the spring, then release them suddenly. Observe the motion of the pieces of tape as you release the coils. Do the pieces of tape move parallel or perpendicular to the direction of motion of the pulse?

The pieces of tape move parallel to the motion of the pulse.

Is this pulse transverse or longitudinal?

The pulse is longitudinal.

12. At this point, you should be quite familiar with how to produce transverse waves. Practice making the following combinations.

	Wave speed	Wave frequency	Wave amplitude
A	High	High	Large
B	High	Low	Large
C	High	High	Small
D	High	Low	Small
E	Low	High	Large
F	Low	High	Small
G	Low	Low	Large
H	Low	Low	Small

To create high-speed waves, students should increase the tension on the spring. To create high-frequency waves, students should create many pulses per second. To create large-amplitude waves, students should move their hands farther back and forth as they generate the pulses.

13. When you are certain you know how to produce each type of wave, call your teacher over. Your teacher will ask you to demonstrate one of the wave types from the above chart.

We accurately performed wave _____ (A—H) from the chart above.

_____ Teacher Signature

Chapter 13: Oscillations and Waves • Simple Harmonic Motion

Chapter 13 Lab   Simple Pendulum

Purpose

In this lab, you will study the effect of length, mass, and amplitude on the period of a simple pendulum.

Time to Set Up: <1 h
Time in Lab: 1 h
Quantitative Lab

Discussion

A motion that repeats itself over and over is referred to as periodic. In many instances, periodic motion results when an object is displaced from its equilibrium position and then released. This is the case with a simple pendulum. A simple pendulum consists of a small object, often called the bob, suspended by a light cord.

Simple harmonic motion is a type of periodic motion in which the restoring force is directly proportional to the displacement. A pendulum moves with simple harmonic motion because a restoring force acts on it that is approximately proportional to the angle of displacement.

The mass of a simple pendulum is taken as the mass of the bob. The length of the pendulum is the distance from the attached end of the cord to the center of mass of the bob. The amplitude of the pendulum is the angle formed by a vertical line and the cord when the bob reaches its maximum outward displacement. The pendulum's period is the time required to complete one full cycle of the motion.

Materials

• set of hooked masses
• 1.2-m-long cord
• pendulum clamp
• meter stick
• stopwatch
• protractor
• ringstand
• C clamp

Procedure

Part A: Dependence of Period on Length

1. Set up the apparatus as shown in the following figure.

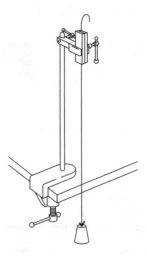

2. Attach a 0.100 kg mass to one end of the cord.

3. Insert the other end of the cord into the pendulum clamp. Adjust the length of the cord so that the distance between the point of attachment and the center of the mass is 1 m.

4. To set the amplitude of the pendulum, hold the protractor next to the cord and displace the mass 5° from the vertical. Release the mass and measure the time it takes the pendulum to complete 10 complete swings. Enter this time in Data Table 1.

5. Repeat steps 3 and 4 using pendulum lengths of 0.8, 0.6, 0.4, and 0.2 m while keeping the mass and amplitude constant. Enter the data in Data Table 1.

Part B: Dependence of Period on Mass of Pendulum Bob

1. Attach a 0.100 kg mass to one end of the cord.

2. Adjust the length of the cord so that the distance between the point of attachment and the center of the mass is 1 m.

3. Using the protractor, displace the mass 5° from the vertical. Release the mass and measure the time it takes the pendulum to complete 10 swings. Enter this time in Data Table 1.

4. Repeat steps 1—3 using pendulum bobs having masses of 0.2, 0.3, 0.4, and 0.5 kg while keeping the length and amplitude constant. Enter the data in Data Table 2.

Part C: Dependence of Period on Amplitude

1. Attach a 0.100 kg mass to one end of the cord.

2. Adjust the length of the cord so that the distance between the point of attachment and the center of the mass is 1 m.

3. Displace the mass 10° from the vertical. Release the mass and measure the time it takes the pendulum to complete 10 swings. Enter this time in Data Table 1.

4. Repeat steps 1—3 for amplitudes of 10°, 20°, 30°, and 40° while keeping the mass and length constant. Enter the data in Data Table 3.

Data

Data Table 1			
Length of pendulum (m)	Time for 10 swings (s)		
	Trial 1	Trial 2	Trial 3
1.0			
0.8			
0.6			
0.4			
0.2			

Data Table 2			
Mass of pendulum bob (kg)	Time for 10 swings (s)		
	Trial 1	Trial 2	Trial 3
0.1			
0.2			
0.3			
0.4			
0.5			

Data Table 3			
Amplitude (degrees)	Time for 10 swings (s)		
	Trial 1	Trial 2	Trial 3
10			
20			
30			
40			
50			

Analysis

1. Calculate the average time for 10 swings and the time for 1 swing (the period) for each trial in Parts A, B, and C and enter in Table 4, 5, and 6, respectively.

2. Using data from Table 4, plot the period of the pendulum versus the pendulum's length.

This graph should represent a square root function.

3. Using data from Table 5, plot the period of the pendulum versus the pendulum's mass.

This graph should be a horizontal line, as mass does not affect the period of the pendulum.

4. Using data from Table 6, plot the period of the pendulum versus the pendulum's amplitude.

Although there is a slight dependence on amplitude, given the precision of the equipment used, students may find this graph to be a horizontal line.

5. Using data from Table 4, plot the period squared versus the pendulum's length.

This graph should be a straight line.

Table 4		
Length of pendulum (m)	Average time for 10 swings (s)	Period (s)

Table 5		
Mass of pendulum bob (m)	Average time for 10 swings (s)	Period (s)

Table 6		
Amplitude (degrees)	Average time for 10 swings (s)	Period (s)

Conclusions

1. Cite any assumptions made in performing this experiment regarding the properties of a simple pendulum.

The main assumption made was that the mass of the string has no effect on the

period of the pendulum.

2. Of the three variables associated with the simple pendulum (length, mass, and amplitude), which variable has the greatest influence on the period?

The length of the pendulum has the greatest influence on the period.

Which variables, if any, seem to have no influence on the period?

The mass has no effect on the period. The amplitude has a small effect on the

period, but students may not observe this in this lab.

3. If you discovered that the period does vary with amplitude, determine the percent change in period from the smallest amplitude to the largest amplitude.

There may be as much as a 5% change between periods for the smallest and largest

amplitudes.

4. Describe the shape of the T versus L graph.

The graph represents a square root function.

How does this differ from the shape of the T^2 versus L graph?

The T^2 versus L graph is a straight line.

What does this tell you about the dependence of the period on the length of the pendulum?

The period depends on the square root of the length of the pendulum.

_____

5. How do you think your results would change (if at all) if you performed this experiment on the moon?

The period of the pendulum would increase due to the reduced

gravitational field on the moon.

6. List possible sources of error in this experiment.

Students may cite timing and measuring the length of the pendulum.

_____

Chapter 13: Oscillations and Waves • Period of an Oscillating Spring
Chapter 13 Lab   Predicting the Period

Your Task

Your teacher will give you a spring. You must determine the period of oscillation for your spring. You may not use a timing device during this phase of the experiment. When ready, ask your teacher to provide the mass that will hang from your spring. You will have 5 minutes to predict the period of oscillation for the spring when the mass is hanging from it.

Equipment Provided

• spring

• mass

Requirements

• You must design an experiment to solve the problem.

• You may request additional equipment from your instructor.

• You will submit an equipment list and procedure before taking any data.

• You will only get one chance to ask for equipment. Make sure your list is complete.

• Your procedure should be thorough enough that another student in the class could follow your instructions.

• Present your data in tables, if appropriate.

• Show calculations used to solve the problem, if applicable.

• List at least two sources of error. For each, indicate what effect the error would have on your results.

Materials Requested

Students may ask for spring scales, digital scales, known masses, and meter

sticks. Students should not be given stopwatches until they have made their

predictions.

_____

_____

_____

Procedure Followed

Students should begin by determining the spring constant of their spring.

When given the mass to hang from their spring, they can then use the

Time to Set Up: <1 h
Time in Lab: 1 h
Performance Assessment

Students will need to determine the spring constant before they can solve for the period of the spring/mass system.

equation for the period of an oscillating mass on a spring to predict the period of oscillation.

_____

_____

_____

_____

_____

_____

Data Collected

Conclusion

_____

_____

_____

_____

Sources of Error

Possible sources of error include:

• The springs might not be 100% Hookean.

• If oscillations are too large, the spring may stretch beyond its elastic limit.

• Students' reaction times will affect the timing of the period of the spring.

Chapter 14 Lab Exploring Sound and Sound Sources

Purpose
In this lab, you will explore some facets of sound production, propagation, and perception of sound.

Time to Set Up: <1 h
Time in Lab: 1 h
Qualitative Lab

Discussion
Vibration is the source of all sound. Tuning forks, vocal cords, violin strings, loudspeaker cones, and bees' wings all produce sound as they vibrate. Vibrating objects disturb the surrounding air, producing waves. These waves travel outward from the source at speeds that are determined by the material, or medium, through which they travel. Like all waves, sound waves are characterized by their amplitude, frequency, and wavelength. The act of detecting and perceiving sound—that is, hearing—is an amazing and extremely complicated process that involves both the ear and the brain.

Materials
Necessary materials will be found at each station.

Procedure

Station 1: Slow Motion Tuning Fork
Adjust the strobe frequency so that it is just above or below 128 Hz. After striking the tuning fork with the rubber mallet, hold the tuning fork in front of the strobe light. Describe the appearance of the vibrating tuning fork.

The tines will appear to move slowly back and forth.

Equipment
Strobe light, 128 Hz tuning fork, rubber mallet

Set the frequency of the strobe light equal to that of the tuning fork. Once again hold the vibrating tuning fork in front of the strobe light. What do you observe now?

The tines will appear stationary.

Explain why this happens.

The frequency of the vibrating tines equals the frequency of the strobe. As a result, the tines are seen in the same location each time the strobe flashes.

Station 2: Vibrating Meter Stick
Use your hand to hold one end of a meter stick down on a table top. The other end should protrude over the edge of the table. With your other hand, set the meter stick into vibration by displacing, and then releasing,

Equipment
Meter stick

its free end. Repeat the procedure, this time with a shorter portion of the meter stick protruding over the edge of the table. Compare the sounds produced by the two lengths of meter stick.

The shortened meter stick vibrates with a higher frequency and produces a

higher-pitched sound.

Continue shortening and plucking the meter stick. What relationship exists between length and pitch for a meter stick?

The pitch is inversely related to the length of the meter stick.

Do you think this relationship holds for other vibrating objects? If so, give some examples.

This relationship holds for other vibrating objects, such as violin strings and

xylophone bars.

Station 3: Singing Glass

Equipment
Wine glass

Hold the wine glass securely by its base on the table with one hand while running the moistened index fingertip of your other hand around the rim of the glass. Can you get the glass to sing? If not, try adjusting the pressure you apply to the rim. Why does the glass produce a sound?

The fingertip repeatedly catches and slips, moving around the rim of the

glass in a series of jerks. These movements "pluck" the rim of the glass,

making the glass vibrate.

Try using different amounts of water in the glass. Do you notice any difference in the sound you hear? If so, why do you think this happens?

When more water is added to the glass, the pitch becomes lower. This

occurs because of an increase in the mass of the glass-water system.

Station 4: Media Matter

Equipment
Barbecue grill grate or similar metal object, string

Pick up the barbecue grill grate by the strings. With the grate hanging by the strings, have your lab partner tap the grill with a pencil. Describe the sound you hear.

A soft, tinny ringing sound is heard.

How does the sound produced by the vibrating grate reach your ears?

The sound reaches the ears through the air.

Now, with your index fingers, place the ends of the strings on the little flap of flesh that protrudes over the opening of each ear. Allowing the grate to hang freely from the strings, again have your lab partner strike it. Describe the sound you hear with the strings pressed against your ears.

The sound is much louder and richer, like the sound of a bell.

How is the sound reaching your ears?

The sound reaches the ears through the strings.

How do you explain the difference in sound quality?

The string transmits a wider range of frequencies much more efficiently

than does the air.

Station 5: Twirly Tube ⚠️

Hold one end of the plastic tube in one hand and swing the other end over your head. Start out swinging the tube slowly, then speed up. (**Be certain that no one is in the immediate area before you start swinging the tube.**) Describe what you hear.

Sounds with higher pitches are heard as the tube is swung faster and faster.

Equipment
Corrugated plastic tube

What do you think is producing the sounds you hear?

As the air passes through the tube, it strikes the ridges that line the tube,

producing sound.

How does increasing the speed with which you twirl the tube change the frequency you hear?

Increasing the rate of twirling causes air to be drawn through the tube at a

higher speed. As air speeds up, the frequency of sound produced by the air's

interaction with the tube walls also increases, creating a higher-pitched sound.

Can you produce any pitch you wish, or can only certain sounds be produced?

Because the length of the air column determines the frequencies that are

reinforced, only certain rates of twirling will produce audible, sustainable sound.

Station 6: Resonant Tuning Forks

Face the open ends of the two boxes with tuning forks toward each other. Strike one of the tuning forks with the rubber mallet. Wait a few seconds, and then touch the tines of the struck tuning fork to stop it from vibrating. What do you hear?

The tuning fork that was initially silent is now vibrating.

Equipment
Resonant tuning fork set, rubber mallet, ping-pong ball

Why do you think this happened?

Vibrations were transferred through the air via sound waves to the second

tuning fork.

Repeat the above procedure, but this time suspend a ping-pong ball so it is lightly touching the tuning fork you don't strike. Describe what happens.

Vibrations set the ping-pong ball into motion.

Change the frequency of one of the tuning forks by attaching the metal clip around one of the tines. Pair it with the other box-mounted tuning fork in the same way as before. Strike the tuning fork without the attached metal clip, and after a moment stop it by touching it. What do you hear?

No sound is heard from either tuning fork.

Why do you think this happened?

Sound waves from the first fork no longer push on the tines of the second fork at the right frequency.

Station 7: And the Beat Goes On

Equipment
Resonant tuning fork set, rubber mallet, two combs with differently spaced teeth

Part A: Face the open ends of the two boxes with tuning forks toward each other. Change the frequency of one of the tuning forks by attaching the metal clip around one of the prongs. What do you hear when you tap both tuning forks?

The two tuning forks combined produce a sound with a slow variation in the volume.

Propose an explanation for the sound produced by the two tuning forks.

The sound waves of slightly different frequency result in alternating constructive and destructive interference. This causes the sound to be alternately loud and soft.

Part B: Overlap the combs. Describe what you see.

A pattern of light and dark: light where gaps between teeth line up, dark where a tooth and a gap overlap.

How does the pattern produced by the two overlapping combs relate to the sound produced by the two tuning forks?

The unequal spacing of teeth on the two combs represents sounds with different frequencies. The pattern of light and dark regions suggests constructive and destructive interference.

Station 8: Doppler Ball ⚠️

Equipment
9-volt buzzer, 9-volt battery, Wiffle ball, strong string, paper

Turn on the buzzer inside the ball. Listen carefully and note the pitch the buzzer produces. Have your lab partner twirl the ball around in a circle above his or her head. Describe the pitch of the ball as it moves toward and away from you. Now listen to the ball as your lab partners throw the ball back and forth in front of you. What do you hear as the ball approaches and recedes from you?

The pitch is higher, compared to the pitch of the ball when stationary, as

the ball approaches and lower as it recedes.

Explain your observations.

Movement of the source changes the wavelength of the sound. It becomes

longer as the source recedes and shorter as the source approaches. This

changes the frequency with which the waves reach the observer.

The Doppler ball consists of a small sound source, such as a piezoelectric buzzer, and a battery packed tightly with paper inside a Wiffle ball. The buzzer and 9-volt battery are available from electronics supply outlets.

Chapter 14 Lab Measuring the Speed of Sound

Purpose

In this lab, you will use a microphone and computer interface to determine the speed of sound in air.

Time to Set Up: <1 h
Time in Lab: <1 h
Quantitative Lab

Discussion

The speed of sound in air is relatively fast. If you clap your hands while standing in front of a wall, the sound will reflect off the wall and create an echo. Because sound travels quite quickly, we cannot hear the echo unless we are a large distance from the wall. Dolphins and bats use echoes to determine the position of objects in their path. In this lab, we will use a computer to detect echoes that occur too quickly for the unaided ear to hear.

Materials

- long, hollow tube with one end closed
- meter stick
- computer and interface
- sound probe
- temperature sensor

Carpet tubes work well. Times will depend on the length of the tubes used, but in general they are quite small (0.005—0.018 second). You will need to help the students set up the time axes on the computer interface so they see the echo on the graph.

Procedure

1. Place the tube on a table with the microphone at the opening of the tube.

2. Set up the computer to measure the sound intensity.

3. Set up the interface so that your clap will initiate the data collection.

4. Practice clapping at the opening of the tube.

5. You should see two "blips": one for the initial clap and, later, another that is smaller in amplitude and is the echo. You may need to adjust the time scale on your screen until you can clearly see both "blips."

6. Measure the length of the tube and record this value in the data section.

7. Determine the temperature of the air inside the tube by placing the temperature probe inside it.

8. Clap at the entrance of the tube. Use the computer tools to determine the elapsed time between the initial clap and the echo. Record this value in Data Table 1.

9. Repeat step 8 three more times. Record your times in Data Table 1.

Data

Length of tube: _____ m
Air temperature: _____°C

Data Table 1	
Trial	Elapsed time (s)
1	
2	
3	
4	

Analysis

1. Calculate the average elapsed time and record this value here. Avg elapsed time _____ (s)

2. The sound wave travels down to the end of the tube and back. Therefore, the total distance traveled during the elapsed time is twice the length of the tube. Record that value here:

   Total distance traveled by sound wave: _____m

3. Determine the speed of sound using the equation $v = d/t$. Record the value here: Experimental speed of sound in air: _____ m/s

Conclusions

1. The speed of sound in air can be calculated using the equation $v = 331 + 0.6T$, where T is the air temperature. Use this equation and your measured air temperature to determine the accepted speed of sound inside the tube.

   Accepted speed of sound: _____ m/s

2. Determine the percent error between your experimental speed of sound and the accepted speed of sound found in step 1 above.

   _____

3. How would your data change if you filled the tube with a different gas, such as carbon dioxide?

   The speed of a wave depends on the medium. Therefore, we would need to know

   if sound traveled faster or slower in the new gas. If sound traveled faster, the times

   would be shorter. If sound traveled slower, the times would be longer.

4. How would your data change if we warmed the air in the tube with a hair dryer?

This would increase the speed of sound in the air, so our times would be shorter.

_____

5. How could you use the procedures from this lab to measure the length of an unknown tube?

If you know the temperature of the air in the tube and the time of the echo, you can determine the length of the tube. You would use $v = 331 + 0.6T$ to determine the speed and $d = vt$ to find the total distance traveled by the sound wave. The length of the tube will be half this amount because the wave traveled down and back.

Chapter 14: Sound • Using Sound to Find Air Temperature

Chapter 14 Lab   What's the Temperature?

Your Task

Your teacher will give you a tuning fork. You must design an experiment that uses the tuning fork to determine the temperature of the air in the classroom.

Equipment Provided

• tuning fork

Requirements

• You must design an experiment to solve the problem.

• You may request additional equipment from your instructor.

• You will submit an equipment list and procedure before taking any data.

• You will only get one chance to ask for equipment. Make sure your list is complete.

• Your procedure should be thorough enough that another student in the class could follow your instructions.

• Present your data in tables, if appropriate.

• Show calculations used to solve the problem, if applicable.

• List at least two sources of error. For each, indicate what effect the error would have on your results.

Materials Requested

Students may ask for large graduated cylinders, beakers, water, and meter
sticks.

_____

_____

_____

_____

_____

Procedure Followed 🔦

Students should change the length of the graduated cylinder by adding
or removing water. They can then find two adjacent lengths at which their
tuning fork resonates. Knowing that the difference in the lengths of these
air columns is 0.5λ, students can determine the wavelength. Then, with the

---

Time to Set Up: <1 h
Time in Lab: 1 h
Performance Assessment

Students will need to determine the speed of sound using the tuning fork frequency and wavelength. They can then use $v = 331 + 0.6T$ to determine the temperature of the room.

Be sure to give students tuning forks with large frequencies (500 Hz+) so that wavelengths are small enough to measure in a graduated cylinder.

frequency of the fork, they can solve for the speed of sound using $v = f\lambda$ and finally use this speed to determine the temperature of the room.

_____

_____

_____

_____

Data Collected

Conclusion

_____

_____

_____

_____

Sources of Error

Possible sources of error include:

• If the water used in the cylinder is hot or cold, the temperature of the air in the cylinder will not be the same as the air temperature in the room.

• The resonant lengths may not be exact.

• The tuning fork may not be exactly at the frequency it is supposed to be.

Chapter 15: The Properties of Light • Color and the Electromagnetic Spectrum

Chapter 15 Lab   Exploring Color and the Electromagnetic Spectrum

Purpose

In this lab, you will explore the nature of electromagnetic waves.

Time to Set Up: <1 h
Time in Lab: <1 h
Qualitative Lab

Discussion

Visible light represents only a small portion of a continuum of radiation known as the electromagnetic spectrum. Consisting of oscillating electric and magnetic fields, all electromagnetic waves found in the spectrum are fundamentally the same. Electromagnetic waves are produced by oscillating electrical charges or electronic transitions in atoms, and all travel at the same speed, namely, the speed of light. They differ only in their frequency and wavelength. At one end of the spectrum are radio waves having wavelengths of thousands of meters. At the other end are electromagnetic waves with extremely short wavelengths. Sometimes referred to as gamma rays, these waves have wavelengths that are smaller than a billionth of a meter.

Materials

Necessary materials will be found at each station.

Procedure

Station 1: Compact Disk Spectroscope ⚠

Look at the unlabeled side of a compact disk (CD). Using the CD like a mirror, tilt it until you can see reflected light from one of the available sources. **WARNING: Do not use the sun as a light source in this activity.** Adjust the angle of the CD until you can see a spectrum. Describe the colors you see in the spectrum. Now look at a different light source. Compare the spectra of the two sources.

Spectra observed will depend on the light sources used. Incandescent

sources produce a continuous spectrum, whereas a compact fluorescent

lamp's spectrum is discrete.

Equipment
Compact disk, various light sources

Emphasize to students that they are not to view reflected light from the sun. The light sources should be small. Small decorative holiday lights, single LEDs, and compact fluorescent lamps viewed from a distance work well.

Station 2: Color Mixing

Place the magnifying glass close to a white area on the screen. Adjust the viewing distance until you see an array of colored dots. Describe the

Equipment
Television or computer monitor, magnifying glass

colors of these dots. Now use the magnifying glass to examine different colored areas on the screen. Describe the color of the dots producing each colored area.

Red, green, and blue dots will be seen in white areas of the screen. The color

of the dots found in other areas of the screen will vary, depending on the

appearance of the area examined. Red, green, or blue areas will have only

red, green, or blue dots, respectively. Magenta, yellow, and cyan areas will

have red and blue, red and green, and blue and green dots, respectively.

Station 3: Seeing beyond the Visible

Equipment
Television remote control, digital camera

Look at the output end of a television remote control while pressing one of the remote's buttons. What do you observe? Now direct the remote control toward the lens of the digital camera. What do you observe on the LCD screen?

A flashing spot of light will be seen. The digital camera's CCD

(chargecoupled device), which converts light into an electrical signal, is

sensitive to infrared light.

Station 4: Detecting Infrared Radiation

Equipment
Three alcohol thermometers, copy-paper box, prism, sheet of white paper

The apparatus for this station consists of a cardboard copy-paper box with a sheet of white paper placed on its bottom. A prism attached to the edge of the box is used to project the sun's spectrum onto the three thermometer bulbs.

Place the box with prism attached in the sun. Position the box and prism so that the sun's spectrum falls on the sheet of paper. After observing the readings on the three thermometers, place the thermometers side by side in the spectrum with the bulb of the thermometer on the left in the blue part of the spectrum, the middle bulb in the yellow part of the spectrum, and the right bulb just past the red part of the spectrum in a region where there is no visible light. Observe and compare the thermometer readings for several minutes. Which thermometer shows the greatest reading? How do you explain this result?

The thermometer located just past the red part of the visible light spectrum,

which is exposed to infrared radiation, should show the highest reading.

Station 5: Detecting Ultraviolet Radiation

Equipment
UV beads

The beads are inexpensive and readily available from most science supply houses. In addition to detecting ultraviolet light, UV beads may be used to test the effectiveness of sunglasses, sun tan lotions, and ordinary glass in absorbing ultraviolet radiation.

Observe the color of the ultraviolet-light-detecting beads. Now take the beads outdoors where they can be exposed to the sun. Describe any changes in the color of the beads. Why do you suppose exposure to sunlight brings about this change? What happens to the color of the beads when they are taken inside?

The normally white beads change color when exposed to ultraviolet

radiation. When taken outdoors, they change color almost immediately.

They return to white when taken inside.

Station 6: Glue Stick Scattering and Polarization

Direct the light from the flashlight into the end of a clear glue stick. Describe the color of the glue stick along its length and at the end opposite the light source. Now place a polarizer between the light source and the glue stick. Describe what happens to the intensity of the light along the length of the glue stick and at its end as the filter is rotated. What might be an explanation for what you observe?

Like the earth's atmosphere, the glue stick scatters blue light more efficiently

than red light. Therefore, from the side the glue stick appears bluish; and with

much of the blue light removed from the white beam by the time the light

reaches the end of the glue stick, the end appears orange-red. In addition,

as is the case with atmospheric scattering, the light is polarized as it passes

through the glue stick. Rotating the polarizer causes an alternating dimming

and brightening of the light along the length of the glue stick and at its end.

Equipment
Glue stick, Mini-Maglite or LED flashlight, polarizer

Station 7: Measuring the Speed of Light in a Microwave Oven

Cover the surface of a paper plate with a thin coating of Marshmallow Fluff. Place the plate in a microwave oven. Cook until you see areas on the surface of the Fluff turning brown. After removing the plate, measure the distance between centers of adjacent brown areas (these are antinodes of the standing wave established in the oven). An average should be taken of three or four of these distances. To find the speed of the wave, use the distance between antinodes (remembering that this is 0.5λ) and the frequency of the microwave oven (*Note:* this is often 2450 MHz).

Students should find the speed of light to be 3×10^8 m/s, +/−10%.

Equipment
Marshmallow Fluff, paper plate, microwave oven

Station 8: Producing Radio Waves

Tune the radio to some point between stations. Holding the battery near the radio, touch one end of the wire to a battery terminal. Now repeatedly touch the other end of the wire to the other battery terminal. (Do not keep both ends of the wire in contact with the battery for a prolonged period. The wire will become hot.) What do you hear? What is causing this sound and how is it produced?

Radio waves are produced as electrons in the wire are briefly accelerated

during the completion of the circuit. The AM radio receives these waves and

converts them into sound.

Equipment
AM radio, 1.5 V battery, wire

Station 9: Radio Wave Polarization

Turn on a handheld AM radio and select a station. Rotate the radio to the right or left until the volume is greatly reduced. Through what angle did you rotate the radio to produce this reduction in volume?

The radio should be rotated through 90°.

Equipment
AM radio

Now continue rotating the radio until the original volume level is restored. Through what angle did you rotate the radio to accomplish this?

A rotation of 90° is required.

Propose an explanation for the dependence of volume level on orientation of the radio.

The electric field of an electromagnetic wave radiated by an AM transmitting antenna is vertically polarized. For maximum absorption of energy from the field, the radio's receiving antenna must be aligned with the plane of polarization.

Chapter 15: The Properties of Light • Color Mixing

Chapter 15 Lab   Glowstick Lab

Purpose

In this lab, you will add primary colors of light to determine what secondary colors they produce.

Discussion

Most people become fascinated with color at an early age. Probably at about the time we are given our first box of crayons, we learn the names of colors, realize that we have favorites, and may even discover that colors can be combined to create new hues. Color continues to play an important role in our lives far beyond childhood. It seems that we are constantly faced with color quandaries. What color car should I buy? Does this tie go with my shirt? We see color on the printed page, the television screen, and on an electronic billboard. We go out of our way to see the perfect sunset or are willing to get wet to enjoy a rainbow. However, we rarely think about why things exhibit the colors they do.

Materials

- glowsticks
- box cutter
- plastic pipettes
- toothpicks
- aprons
- gloves
- transparency sheet
- white paper

Procedure

1. Place the transparency sheet on top of a sheet of white paper.

2. Once the lights are off, place one drop of each color on the transparency sheet. You will use these colors for comparison.

3. Mix the following colors together by placing one drop of each (or as instructed by your teacher) together on the same spot on the transparency sheet. Use the toothpick to mix the liquids together.

Mixture 1	Mixture 2	Mixture 3
Red and blue	Red and green	Blue and green

4. In Data Table 1 record the colors you see when the liquids are mixed.

Time to Set Up: <1 h
Time in Lab: <1 h
Qualitative Lab

This lab must be done in a dark room. Activate the glowsticks by breaking their inner tubes. Use the box cutters to open the tubes. Be careful, as there will be broken glass inside the tube. Use the pipettes to suck up the liquid. Do not give students the actual glowsticks, but only the pipettes full of each color.

Glowsticks can be purchased in bulk from most science supply stores. Each class will require approximately four large glowsticks of each color. The liquid inside the glowsticks is not toxic, but it will stain and is quite oily.

Often, the blue liquid is less intense than the red and green, and students may need to use two drops of blue for every drop of the other colors to achieve the desired results.

5. Create three new mixtures by adding the following to each of the mixtures from step 3. Use a toothpick to mix the liquids together.

Mixture 4	Mixture 5	Mixture 6
Mixture 1 + green	Mixture 2 + blue	Mixture 3 + red

6. In Data Table 1 record the colors you see when the liquids are mixed.

Data Table 1		
Mixture 1	Mixture 2	Mixture 3
Magenta	Yellow	Cyan

Mixture 4	Mixture 5	Mixture 6
White	White	White

Analysis and Conclusions

1. What is the name given to red, green, and blue light?
Primary colors

2. Why are these three colors important when adding colors of light?
Using these colors in different mixtures, you can make any color of light.

3. What is the name given to the colors produced in mixtures 1—3?
These are secondary colors.

4. Mixtures 4—6 should all be the same color. What colors of liquid were added to all three mixtures?
All the mixtures contain red, blue, and green light.

5. When two colors are added together and produce white light, we call them complementary colors. Name the three complementary color pairs for light.
Magenta + green; yellow + blue; cyan + red

6. Imagine that a painter and a lighting director are having a conversation about mixing colors. Would they agree or disagree about what happens when you mix yellow and blue? Explain.
The painter would say that yellow and blue make green, while the lighting director would say yellow and blue make white. The painter is mixing pigments, and the lighting director is mixing light. Pigments create color by subtraction and light creates color by addition.

Chapter 15: Properties of Light • Color Subtraction

Chapter 15 Lab   Paint for Understanding

Your Task

You will be given a picture of a flag and a description of the light that illuminates it. You must use the inks provided to paint a picture that shows how the flag would look under these lighting conditions.

Equipment Provided

- flag
- paper
- light description
- colored inks
- Q-tips
- mixing tray

Requirements

- Use the inks provided to paint a picture that accurately shows how the flag would appear in the prescribed lighting.
- You are expected to mix appropriate colors. Writing the names of the colors beside them will not be acceptable.

Time to Set Up: <1 h
Time in Lab: 1 h
Performance Assessment

You can design any flag that consists of primary and secondary colors, as well as black and white. You can prescribe what color light shines on the flag or shines through a filter before hitting the flag. For example, cyan light shines through a yellow filter. India inks work well. You will need cyan (sometimes called teal), yellow, and magenta. Students can use these to mix red, green, blue, and black.

Chapter 16: Reflection and Mirrors • **Reflection**

Chapter 16 Lab   Exploring Reflection

Purpose

In this lab, you will investigate the phenomenon of reflection and its applications.

Time to Set Up: <1 h
Time in Lab: 1 h
Qualitative Lab

Discussion

We rely on reflected light to see most objects in our environment. This page, your face in a mirror, and the moon are made visible through reflection. The reflection of light from a smooth surface, such as calm water, a highly polished table top, or a mirror, is called specular reflection. Specular reflection results in clear, well-defined likenesses of objects called images. All specular reflectors produce images in the same way. Light rays originating at an object travel to the reflector's surface, where they bounce off in a well-defined way. When the reflected rays are extended, they intersect, or appear to intersect, at a point that defines the position of the image.

When light reflects off an optically rough surface, such as a piece of cloth, it diffuses—that is, it scatters in all directions. This diffuse reflection does not result in a clear image. You can see a piece of cloth, but you cannot see your image in the cloth. Specular and diffuse reflection have distinctly different applications. Shaving or putting on makeup would be difficult without specular reflection. On the other hand, using a mirror as a movie screen would not be prudent, for most of the audience wouldn't receive any light while others would receive way too much. As a consequence, movie screens are diffuse reflectors.

Materials

Necessary materials will be found at each station.

Procedure

Station 1: Sizing Up Your Image

How does the size of the image of your head compare to its actual size?

The size of the image appears equal to the size of the object.

How does the observed size of your image change as you move away from the mirror? To find out, use a washable marker to draw an outline of your head on the surface of the mirror. Now move away from the mirror, all the while keeping the image of your face within the outline.

Equipment
Plane mirror

How does the size of the image of your head compare to the size of the circle as you move farther from the mirror?

The head continues to fill the outline regardless of distance from the mirror.

Both the distance from the image and the distance from the mirror's surface

increase at the same rate, making the change in the apparent size of the

outline and image the same.

Station 2: Perceived Depth

Equipment
6-inch ruler, plane mirror

Place one end of the ruler up against, and perpendicular to, the mirror's surface. How does the length of the image of the ruler compare to the actual length of the ruler?

They appear to be the same.

How far behind the mirror does the image of the ruler extend?

The image of the ruler appears to extend 6 inches behind the mirror.

How does the writing on the ruler appear in the mirror?

The writing is reversed.

Station 3: Single Ray Reflection

Equipment
Ray box, adjustable ray slit mask, plane mirror, paper

Place the ray box on a sheet of white paper. Insert the single-slit mask in the ray box. Position the plane mirror perpendicular to the paper. Using the mirror as a straight edge, mark the mirror's position on the paper. Project a ray of light at an angle onto the mirror's surface. How does the angle formed by the incoming ray and the mirror's surface appear to compare to the angle formed by the reflected ray and the mirror's surface? To check your answer, make two dots on the paper along the incoming ray and two dots on the reflected ray. After connecting each pair of dots with a straight line, use a protractor to measure the angles the lines make with the mirror.

The two angles are congruent.

Change the angle between the incoming ray and the mirror. How does the angle formed by the incoming ray and the mirror's surface compare to the angle formed by the reflected ray and the mirror's surface now?

They are congruent.

Station 4: Mirror Multiplication

Equipment
Two plane mirrors taped together to form a hinge, small object, e.g., a coin

Arrange the mirrors so that they form a right angle. Place a small object, such as a coin, between the hinged mirrors. Observe the images formed by the mirrors. How many images do you see?

Three images are produced.

Observe the writing on the coins. Does the writing on all the coin images appear normal? If not, on which coin or coins does the writing appear normal? Explain why this is so.

The corner image is the only one whose writing is not reversed. Images

formed by a single reflection will be reversed. Images that are formed as the

result of two reflections, such as the corner image, will appear normal.

What happens when you make the angle between the mirrors smaller?

As the angle decreases, the number of images increases.

Station 5: A View of Infinity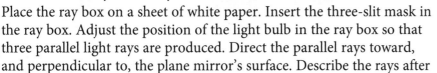

Place the two mirrors 10 to 15 centimeters apart with their reflective surfaces facing each other. After placing a coin between the mirrors, adjust the mirrors so that they are parallel to each other. Look past the back edge of one mirror into the other. Describe the images produced.

The images are numerous and seem to stretch into the distance. The number

of images produced is limited by the absorption of light by the mirrors.

Equipment
Two plane mirrors, small object, e.g., a coin

Station 6: Waterproof Flame

Look into the glass at the candle that seems to be burning under water. How is this possible?

The positions of the glass of water and the image of the candle are the same.

Move the candle farther away from the glass. What must you do to the glass of water to keep the candle "under water"? What does this tell you about image and object distances?

The glass of water must be moved farther away from the glass. Image and

object distances are equal.

Equipment
Sheet of plexiglass, glass of water, wax or LED candle

Assembly
Place the glass of water on the far side of the plexiglass. Place the lit candle equidistant in front of the plexiglass so that when viewed from the front, the image of the candle appears inside the glass of water.

Station 7: Plane, Concave, and Convex Mirrors

Place the ray box on a sheet of white paper. Insert the three-slit mask in the ray box. Adjust the position of the light bulb in the ray box so that three parallel light rays are produced. Direct the parallel rays toward, and perpendicular to, the plane mirror's surface. Describe the rays after reflection from the mirror.

The rays are reflected back on the incoming rays.

Direct the three parallel rays so that they strike the plane mirror at an angle. Describe the rays after reflection from the mirror.

The rays remain parallel but reflect off at an angle.

Equipment
Ray box; adjustable ray slit mask; paper; plane, concave, and convex mirrors

Direct the three parallel rays toward the center of the concave mirror. Describe the rays after reflection from the mirror.

The reflected rays converge to a point after reflection.

Direct the three parallel rays toward the center of the convex mirror. Describe the rays after reflection from the mirror.

The reflected rays diverge after reflection.

Equipment
Sheet of glass, sheet of paper

Station 8: "X" Marks the Spot 🧪

Place the sheet of glass in the center of and perpendicular to the paper. Draw an X on the paper, on the side of the glass nearest you. Now, looking into the glass, trace over the image of the X on the paper on the opposite side of the glass. Describe the location and size of the image.

The image X has the same size as the object X and is located at the same

distance behind the glass as the object X is in front of it.

Equipment
Sheet of smooth aluminum foil

Station 9: Specular or Diffuse?

Describe what you see when you hold your hand over the smooth aluminum foil. Crumple and then straighten out the foil. Describe what you see now.

The smooth foil is a specular reflector and produces a clear image. Once the foil

is crumpled, it becomes a diffuse reflector and does not produce a clear image.

Chapter 16 Lab   Reflection by Multiple Mirrors

Purpose

In this lab, you will (1) determine the relationship between the angle between two hinged mirrors and the number of images produced, and (2) construct a simple kaleidoscope.

Time to Set Up: <1 h
Time in Lab: 1 h
Quantitative Lab

Discussion

An image is formed each time light from an object reflects from a plane mirror. When two mirrors are placed edge to edge at an angle, some light may reflect back and forth between the mirrors. These multiple reflections give rise to multiple images. The number of images produced depends on the angle between the mirrors. The kaleidoscope is a device that uses mirrors to produce multiple images.

Materials

- two large, hinged plane mirrors
- two microscope slides
- electrical tape
- protractor
- small object
- beads
- sheet of cardboard

Hinge the mirrors together using duct tape.

Procedure 🔧

Part A: Investigating Image Formation by Two Mirrors

1. Extend the mirrors so they form a 180° angle, i.e., a straight line.

2. Place a small object, such as a coin, in front of the mirrors and observe the number of images produced. Record the number of images produced in Data Table 1.

3. Use a protractor to adjust the mirrors so they form a 120° angle. Record the number of images produced in Data Table 1.

4. Repeat step 3 with angles of 90°, 60°, 45°, 30°, and 20°.

Part B: Constructing a Kaleidoscope

1. Clean two microscope slides.

2. Trace the outline of one of the slides on a piece of thick cardboard.

3. Use scissors to cut out a slide-shaped section of cardboard. This will serve as a spacer between the two slides.

4. Place the two slides and spacer on a flat surface with the long edges parallel to each other. A small gap should be left between each of the three components so that they can later be folded into a triangle (see figure).

Either glass or plastic microscope slides work well.

5. Connect the slides and spacer to each other by placing lengths of electrical tape over the gaps.

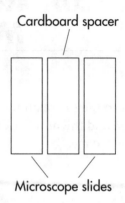

Cardboard spacer

Microscope slides

6. Form a triangle out of the slides and cardboard by bringing the outer edges of the two slides together. Tape the edges of the slides together.

7. Cover the outer surfaces of the slides with electrical tape. This completes the construction of the essential elements of what is known as a teleidoscope.

8. View a variety of objects, such as a book or clothing, through the teleidoscope.

9. Stretch and tape plastic wrap over one end of the teleidoscope.

10. Drop a few colored beads into the open end of the teleidoscope.

11. Stretch and tape a piece of plastic wrap across the open end of the teleidoscope and secure it with tape. This completes construction of your kaleidoscope.

12. Look down into the kaleidoscope. Watch the changing patterns as you rotate the kaleidoscope.

Usually, adding just a few beads, e.g., three or four, gives the best results.

Suggest that students aim their kaleidoscopes directly at a light source. They should never use the sun as a source of light.

Data

Data Table 1		
Angle (θ)	Number of images (N)	360°/θ
180°	1	2
120°	2	3
90°	3	4
60°	5	6
45°	7	8
30°	11	12
20°	17	18

Analysis and Conclusions

Part A

1. What happened to the number of images as the angle between the mirrors decreased? Explain why this occurred.

   The number of images increased as the angle between the mirrors decreased

   because the number of reflections between mirrors increased.

2. How does the ratio of 360°/θ compare to the number of images for each angle?

   The ratio of 360°/θ equals the number of images plus 1.

3. Based on your answer to question 2, state a relationship between the number of images N and the size of the angle θ.

   $N = 360°/θ - 1$

4. Determine the number of images if the angle between the mirrors were reduced to 1°, 0.5°, and 0.1°.

   For 1°, 0.5°, and 0.1° there would be 359, 719, and 3599 images produced, respectively.

Part B

1. Describe the appearance of objects viewed through the teleidoscope.

   Symmetric patterns of objects viewed are produced.

2. What is the angle between the slides in your kaleidoscope?

   The angle between slides is 60°.

3. In theory, how many images of each bead should be produced by the kaleidoscope? Does this agree with what you observe?

   Five images of each bead should be produced.

4. How would image production be affected if the cardboard spacer were replaced with a third slide? Explain your answer.

   Theoretically, an infinite number of reflections would produce an infinite number of

   images. However, the number of visible images is limited by absorption of light by

   each of the mirrors.

Chapter 16 Lab   Put the Picture in the Frame

Time to Set Up: <1 h
Time in Lab: 1 h
Performance Assessment

Your Task

You will be given a light bulb with an arrow drawn on it, a mirror, and a piece of paper with a rectangular frame sketched on it. You must determine where to place the mirror and paper so that the image of the arrow fills the rectangular frame on the paper. You may not turn on your light bulb until you are ready to test your answer.

Equipment Provided

- concave mirror and holder
- light bulb base
- light bulb with arrow drawn on it
- paper with rectangular frame drawn on it

Use a permanent marker to draw arrows on the light bulbs. The rectangular frames can be as large or small as you desire.

Requirements

- You must design an experiment to solve the problem.
- You may request additional equipment from your instructor.
- You will submit an equipment list and procedure before taking any data.
- You will only get one chance to ask for equipment. Make sure your list is complete.
- Your procedure should be thorough enough that another student in the class could follow your instructions.
- Present your data in tables, if appropriate.
- Show calculations used to solve the problem, if applicable.
- List at least two sources of error. For each, indicate what effect the error would have on your results.

Materials Requested

Students may ask for meter sticks and light bulbs without arrows.

_____

_____

_____

_____

_____

Procedure Followed 🔦

Students will need to determine the focal length of the mirror and the required magnification to make the arrow fill the frame. Students may choose to find the location of the image of a distant object to determine the focal length of the mirror. They could also place an object at a known object distance, determine the image distance, and use the mirror equation to determine the focal length. With the magnification and focal length, students can use $M = -d_i/d_o$ and $1/f = 1/d_o + 1/d_i$ to determine the locations of the light bulb and frame.

_____

_____

Data Collected

Conclusion

_____

_____

_____

_____

Sources of Error

Possible sources of error include:

• Focal length is calculated and might be wrong due to uncertainties in the measurements.

• Object might not have been distant enough to have the image at the focus of the mirror.

• The light bulb is curved, and therefore the object distance is not correct for the entire arrow.

Chapter 17 Lab   Exploring Refraction

Purpose

In this lab, you will explore the refraction of light and its applications.

Discussion

When light passes from one transparent material, or medium, into another it may change direction. This bending is called *refraction*. The amount of bending depends on the nature of the two media and on the angle at which the light enters the second medium. Refraction occurs because light travels with different speeds in different media. The ratio of the speed of light in a vacuum to its speed in a given medium is called the medium's index of refraction.

Specially designed pieces of glass or plastic called lenses refract light to form images. Depending on the shapes of its surfaces (convex or concave), a lens, like a mirror, can form either real or virtual images. Lenses are key elements in optical instruments such as eyeglasses, cameras, projectors, microscopes and telescopes, and, of course, the eye. Refraction is also responsible for dispersion, the breaking up of white light into its component colors by a prism.

Procedure

Station 1: Submerged Ruler 🧪

Fill the glass about three-quarters full of water. Insert the ruler vertically into the water. Describe the appearance of the submerged ruler when it is viewed through the side of the glass.

The ruler will appear wider than it actually is.

_____

Explain the appearance of the ruler.

Light leaving the water is bent in such a way as to produce an enlarged

image.

Tilt the submerged ruler. How does the ruler look now?

The ruler and its image seem to separate at the surface of the water.

Propose an explanation for the appearance of the tilted ruler.

The light from the ruler and the light from its image travel along different

paths.

Time to Set Up: <1 h
Time in Lab: 1 h
Qualitative Lab

Equipment
Clear glass or beaker, plastic ruler

Equipment
Small clear drinking glass or beaker, a few water-storing gel marbles (also called "jelly marbles"), water

Assembly
Place a few of the marbles in a glass of water the night before to allow them to absorb the water. Cover the marbles with water before students arrive.

Station 2: Vanishing Act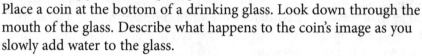

Look at the glass. What do you see inside it?

Students should not be able to see the marbles.

Gently, place your finger into the glass. What do you detect?

The students should feel the marbles in the water.

Explain how this optical illusion was accomplished.

The water and marble have the same index of refraction, and thus there is

no bending as light passes from the water into and out of the marble.

Equipment
Drinking glass, coin, water

Station 3: Apparent Buoyancy

Place a coin at the bottom of a drinking glass. Look down through the mouth of the glass. Describe what happens to the coin's image as you slowly add water to the glass.

The coin appears to rise from the bottom of the glass.

Bring a second similar coin next to the side of the glass. Move the coin up and down until it appears to be at the same height as the submerged coin's image. Have your lab partner measure the depth of the submerged coin and the depth of its image. Calculate the ratio of the actual depth to the apparent depth. Do you suppose this ratio is the same for all submerged objects? Explain your answer.

The ratio should be around 1.33. It will be the same for all objects

submerged in water.

Equipment
Evaporating dish or bowl, coin

Station 4: Reappearing Coin

Place a coin in the bottom of an evaporating dish or bowl. Now move your head to the side until you reach a position where the coin disappears behind the side of the dish. Have your lab partner slowly add water from a beaker to the dish. What do you observe?

The coin becomes visible as water is added to the dish.

Why do you think this happens?

Light from the coin is bent as it exits the water in such a way as to enter the

observer's eyes.

Equipment
Ray box, adjustable ray slit mask, plexiglass block, two double-convex lenses, double-concave lens, prism

Station 5: Studying Refraction with a Ray Box

Send a single ray of light from the ray box through a rectangular block of plastic, first with the ray entering the block along a perpendicular to the block, then at an angle with respect to the surface of the block. Use sketches to show the path of the ray as it (1) enters the block, (2) travels inside the block, and (3) leaves the block for each case.

_____

_____

_____

_____

_____

Using the ray box, send three rays through the rectangular block of plastic, directing them along perpendiculars to the surface of the block. Describe what happens to the light rays as they pass through the block of plastic. That is, does the block converge or diverge the light rays, or does it leave their direction unchanged?

The light rays do not bend as they enter and exit the block. The rays remain

parallel as they pass through the block, so they neither converge nor diverge.

Replace the rectangular block with the thin double-convex plastic lens. Again describe the path of the light rays after they emerge from the lens. Use a sketch in your answer.

The rays converge to a point.

Now use the thick double-convex lens. Describe your observations. Use a sketch in your answer.

The thick lens converges the rays, but does so closer to the lens than does

the thin lens.

Send a number of parallel light rays through a double-concave lens. Describe what happens to the light rays after they leave the lens. Use a sketch in your answer.

The double-concave lens diverges the light rays.

Send a single ray of light into a plastic prism. Can you form a rainbow with the prism?

Yes, light is dispersed into its composite colors as it passes through the prism near one of its vertices.

Equipment
Ray box, adjustable ray slit mask, semicircular glass disk

Station 6: Things Are Getting Critical

Using the ray box, send a single ray of light through the curved side of the semicircular glass disk. Rotate the semicircular disk with the light ray entering the curved surface and aimed at the center of the flat side of the disk. Start with the ray incident nearly perpendicular to the flat internal surface. Slowly rotate the semicircular disk until the light is no longer transmitted through the flat side of the disk. Describe the path of the light ray when this occurs.

The ray is totally internally reflected; that is, it reflects back into the block.

Describe the path of the light ray as you continue rotating the disk.

The ray continues to be totally internally reflected.

Equipment
Piece of wax paper, printed material, water

Station 7: Water Drop Magnifier

Place the wax paper on some printed material. Now place a drop of water on the wax paper. How does the water droplet affect the appearance of the print?

The water droplet will magnify the print.

Why do you suppose this is so?

The water droplet acts as a convex lens.

Equipment
Convex lens, concave lens, index card

Station 8: Convex Lens Cover-up

Hold a convex lens in a dark part of the room so that light from a distant object passes through it and is incident on a screen, such as a white card or piece of paper. Adjust the distance between the lens and screen until you observe a sharp image. Describe the image. Is it right side up or upside down? Is it larger or smaller than the object?

The image is upside down and smaller than the object.

What do you think will happen to the image when you place the index card over a portion of the lens?

Answers will vary.

Use the index card to cover half the lens. How is the image affected?

The entire image will still be seen. The index card may cause the image to dim.

Chapter 17 Lab   Converging Lens

Purpose

In this lab, you will investigate the characteristics and locations of images formed by a thin convex lens. In addition, you will determine the focal length of the lens and look for a relationship between image distance, object distance, and focal length of the lens.

Time to Set Up: <1 h
Time in Lab: 1 h
Quantitative Lab

Discussion

Specially designed pieces of glass or plastic, called lenses, refract light to form images. Lenses are key elements in optical instruments, such as eyeglasses, cameras, projectors, microscopes and telescopes, and, of course, the eye. A lens that is thicker in the center than at the edges is called a convex lens. Convex lenses cause incoming parallel rays to intersect at a common point called the focal point and therefore are also referred to as converging lenses. Diverging lenses are thinner in the center than at the edges and, because they spread light out, are also called diverging lenses.

Materials

- convex lens
- optical bench
- object (e.g., a light bulb or LED tea light)
- lens holder
- screen (index card)

Procedure

1. Measure the height of the object and record it in the data section.

2. Mount the lens holder containing the convex lens on the optical bench. Direct the lens toward a distant object, such as an outdoor landscape or light bulb located at the far end of the room. Adjust the position of the screen until a sharp image of the object is observed on it. Determine the distance between the lens and screen and enter this in the data section as the focal length of the lens. *Note:* All distances are measured with respect to the center of the lens.

3. Use the value for the focal length to compute the object distances for your lens. Record these values in Data Table 1.

4. Place the lens in the center of the optical bench. Position the object at a distance equal to 3.0 focal lengths (3*f*) from the lens. Move the screen back and forth on the side of the lens opposite the object until a sharp image is produced. Record the image distance in Data Table 1.

5. For each object position, measure the height of the image produced. Enter this information in Data Table 1. Also, record the characteristics of the image. These include sense—that is, whether the image is right side up (RSU) or upside down (USD)—and whether the image is real (R) or virtual (V).

6. If it isn't possible to form an image on the screen for certain object distances, the image is virtual or does not exist. To check for a virtual image, look through the lens at the object. You may see a larger, RSU image. You will not be able to accurately determine the image location or height. For these images, simply note the image characteristics.

7. Repeat steps 4 and 5, finding the location and characteristics of the image, when the light source is at object distances equal to 2.5f, 2f, 1.5f, f, and 0.5f. (*Note:* Some of these distances may not work for the lens you were given. If this is the case, you may select your own object distances.)

Data

Focal length of lens_____

Height of object_____

Data Table 1										
Object distance (d_o)	Image distance (d_i)	Image height (h_i)	Sense (RSU or USD)	Real (R) or virtual (V)	$1/d_o$	$1/d_i$	$1/d_o + 1/d_i$	$1/f$	h_i/h_o	d_i/d_o
$3f =$										
$2.5f =$										
$2.0f =$										
$1.5f =$										
$1.0f =$										
$0.5f =$										

Analysis

1. Compute $1/d_o$, $1/d_i$, $1/f$, and $1/d_o + 1/d_i$. Enter these values in Data Table 1 as decimals rounded to the nearest thousandth.

2. Compute h_i/h_o and d_i/d_o and enter in Data Table 1.

Conclusions

1. What mathematical relationship exists between d_o, d_i, and f? Assuming you know d_o and f, what will this relationship, known as the thin lens equation, enable you to do?

$1/d_o + 1/d_i = 1/f$. You can compute the image location.

_____

2. As an object is moved toward a converging lens from a large distance, what changes occur in the size, position, and orientation of the image? Is the image real for all object distances? If not, where does the transition from real to virtual image occur?

The image is real and USD. It gets larger and farther from the lens until you reach the focal point. At the focal point, no image is formed. When the object is located inside the focal point, the image is virtual, RSU, and larger than the object.

3. According to the thin lens equation, where is the image located when an object is placed at a large distance—say, 20 m—from a converging lens?

The image would be located at the focal point of the lens.

4. Where should an object be located with respect to a converging lens so that the object and image distance are equal? Describe the characteristics of the image at this distance.

The object should be placed at twice the focal length. The image is USD, real, and the same size as the object.

5. As an object is moved closer to a lens, does the focal length of the lens increase, decrease, or stay the same? Explain your answer.

The location of the object does not affect the focal length of the lens. The shape and the material from which the lens is made determine the focal length of the lens.

6. How do the ratios h_i/h_o and d_i/d_o compare?

They are equivalent.

Chapter 17: Refraction and Lenses • **Measuring the Speed of Light**

Chapter 17 Lab   What's the Speed?

Your Task

You will be given a tray filled with a transparent substance. You must determine the speed of light in the substance.

Time to Set Up: <1 h
Time in Lab: 1 h
Performance Assessment

Equipment Provided

• semicircular tray filled with transparent substance

Fill the trays with substances such as Karo Syrup, alcohol, or oil.

Requirements

• You must design an experiment to solve the problem.

• You may request additional equipment from your instructor.

• You will submit an equipment list and procedure before taking any data.

• You will only get one chance to ask for equipment. Make sure your list is complete.

• Your procedure should be thorough enough that another student in the class could follow your instructions.

• Present your data in tables, if appropriate.

• Show calculations used to solve the problem, if applicable.

• List at least two sources of error. For each, indicate what effect the error would have on your results.

Materials Requested

Students may ask for ray boxes with single-ray tabs and protractors

_____

_____

_____

_____

_____

Procedure Followed

Students will need to determine the index of refraction of the substance.

They can accomplish this in two ways. They can shine the light into the flat

side of the container and find the refracted angle as the light passes into

the substance. Then, using Snell's law, they can determine the index of refraction. They may also shine the light ray into the circular side of the tray and find the critical angle for the substance/air interface. Then, using $\sin^{-1} \theta = n_2/n_1$, they can determine the index of refraction of the substance. Finally, they must use $n = c/v$ to determine the speed of light in the substance.

_____

_____

Data Collected

Conclusion

_____

_____

_____

_____

Sources of Error

Possible sources of error include:

• Students should do several trials to check the accuracy of their results.

• If the light is not shone on the center of the circle, the angles will not be correct.

Chapter 18 Lab   Exploring Interference and Diffraction

Purpose

In this lab, you will explore interference and diffraction of light waves.

Time to Set Up: 1 h
Time in Lab: 1 h
Qualitative Lab

Discussion

Interference can occur when two or more waves occupy the same region of space at the same time. All types of waves—water, sound, and electromagnetic—are capable of interfering. Interference between light waves results in an increase in brightness for constructive interference and a decrease in brightness for destructive interference. Light waves may interfere after passing through narrow, closely spaced slits or when reflected from thin films. The coloration that sometimes results from the interference of light waves is referred to as iridescence. This optical phenomenon is widespread in both the natural and the manmade world.

Diffraction is defined as the bending of light as it passes through a small opening or around the edge of an object. The passage of light through a small opening or around the edge of an object produces a series of bright and dark fringes called a diffraction pattern. Because diffraction blurs images, it can be difficult to visually separate, or resolve, objects that are very close together.

Materials

Necessary materials will be found at each station.

Procedure

Station 1: Double-Slit Interference

View the showcase bulb through the double slits in the plate. (The slits should be held parallel to the showcase bulb's filament.) Describe what you see.

An interference pattern consisting of alternating multicolored and dark

fringes is observed.

Place the red filter over the showcase bulb and look at the light through the plate again. What do you see now?

An interference pattern consisting of alternating red and dark fringes is

observed.

Equipment
Double-slit plate, showcase bulb, red filter, blue filter

Cover the upper half of the bulb with a red filter and the bottom half with a blue filter. Describe what you see when the bi-colored bulb is viewed through the two slits.

Two interference patterns are observed, one on top of the other. The spacing

between the red fringes is greater than the spacing between the blue fringes.

Station 2: Soap Film Interference Colors

Equipment
Soap solution, dish, 35 mm film canister or black cup

Insert the open end of the film canister into the soap solution. When you remove the canister, a thin soap film should be seen covering the opening. Move the canister around until light is reflected from the surface of the film. What do you observe on the surface of the film?

Bands of color are seen.

Describe what happens as you continue watching the film. Do you observe any changes in the colors produced by the film?

The bands of color move downward.

Eventually, the top of the film will become black. Do you think there is still film in that area? Explain your answer.

There has to be film at the top or the film would burst.

Why does the area at the top of the film appear black?

In the black area, destructive interference results in the cancellation of

waves reflected from the front and back surfaces of the film.

Predict what will happen if a pen tip is inserted in the black area. Now try it and describe what happens.

The film breaks when the pen tip is inserted in the black area.

Station 3: Permanent Thin Film Colors

Equipment
10 cm × 10 cm sheet of black construction paper, colorless nail polish, water-filled tray, prepared sample thin film

Assembly
Follow the student directions and prepare a sample film before class.

Completely submerge a piece of black construction paper in the water. Apply one drop of colorless nail polish to the water above the center of the paper. The nail polish should quickly spread out over the surface of the water. After the nail polish has stopped spreading, slowly lift the construction paper out of the water. The thin film of nail polish should adhere to the surface of the paper. Allow the paper to dry.

Look at the previously prepared thin film sample. What do you observe on the surface of the dried paper?

Rings of colors are seen.

Remembering that the nail polish was colorless, how can you explain the origin of these colors?

The colors are the result of interference between light waves reflecting from

the outside and inside surfaces of the film. These colors are known as iridescent

colors because they appear to change when viewed from different angles.

Station 4: Iridescent Ink

Hold a well-illuminated $20 bill at eye level. Observe the numeral in the lower right-hand corner of the bill as you tilt it back and forth. What do you see?

The numeral appears copper-colored at one angle and bright green at another.

Explain your observations.

Due to interference effects, color-shifting inks reflect various wavelengths

differently, depending on the viewing angle.

Equipment
$10 or $20 bill

Station 5: Diffraction at a Sharp Edge

Hold the edge of the index card between your eye and a bright source of light. Look carefully at the region immediately above the edge of the card. Move the card slowly up and down. Describe what you see. (You may have to bring the card close to your eye.)

A bright line is seen just above the edge of the card.

How do you think this effect is produced?

As the light diffracts around the card, the waves interfere. The bright line is

an area of constructive interference.

Equipment
Source of bright light, index card

Station 6: Diffraction at Your Fingertips

Hold your index and middle finger close together. View the vertical filament in the showcase bulb through a slit formed by your fingers. What do you observe?

A diffraction pattern consisting of a series of dark lines parallel to the fingers

is seen.

Describe what happens as you squeeze your fingers together.

As the slit gets narrower, the dark lines become more distinct.

Equipment
Showcase bulb

Station 7: Gift Wrap Interference

Examine the gift wrap sample. Describe its appearance.

Pastel colors are seen.

What do you observe as you tilt the film?

The colors seen depend on the angle at which the film is viewed.

Equipment
Transparent iridescent gift wrap

Select a particular area of the gift wrap. While holding it in front of your eye, look at the light source. Describe the color of the light transmitted through the area of the film you've selected.

Answers will vary.

Now view the same area by reflected light. Hold the wrap in front of you, parallel to the floor. Describe the color of light reflected by the wrap.

Answers will vary

What relationship exists between the transmitted and reflected light?

The colors are complementary.

Station 8: Resolution

Clip foil A to the ringstand so that it is in front of the bulb. Looking at the holes, move backward until you can see only one hole. Note this location.

Clip foil B to the ringstand and repeat the process above.

How do the distances for foils A and B compare?

You have to move farther back before the holes in foil B appear to merge into one hole.

Repeat the process for foil C. How do the distances for foils A and C compare?

You have to move farther back before the holes in foil C appear to merge into one hole.

Begin by standing close to the picture and then slowly move away. Describe how the image changes as you increase your distance from the picture. Explain.

As you get farther from the picture, the dots merge to create a clear image.

Where do you see this principle in everyday life?

Scoreboards and electronic signs are good examples.

Equipment

40-watt bulb; sheet of aluminum foil, marked A, with two pinholes spaced approximately 0.5 cm apart; sheet of aluminum foil, marked B, with two pinholes spaced 1 cm apart; sheet of aluminum foil, marked C, with two larger holes spaced 0.5 cm apart; ring-stand; clip; domino artwork (search web and print out)

Assembly

Fold a large sheet of aluminum foil over upon itself a few times. Use a pin or needle to pierce the foil as indicated above.

Chapter 18 Lab   Measuring the Wavelength of Light with a Diffraction Grating

Purpose

In this lab, you will use a diffraction grating to determine the wavelength of laser light.

Discussion

In 1801, Thomas Young demonstrated that light from two coherent light sources is capable of interfering. Passing light through two closely spaced slits, Young observed a series of alternating bright and dark lines, or fringes, on a screen. He reasoned that the fringes were a direct result of constructive and destructive interference. This served as the strongest evidence to date in support of the wave theory of light.

Bright fringes, such as those observed by Young, will be produced at locations on a screen that are a whole number of wavelengths farther from one slit than the other. That is, the path length difference = integer × wavelength. The figure on the following page indicates that the path difference is $d \sin \theta$. Thus, the condition for the formation of a bright fringe can be written as $d \sin \theta = m\lambda$, where d is the slit spacing, θ indicates the direction to a given bright fringe, m is the order of the fringe, and λ is the wavelength of light. The value $m = 0$ corresponds to the central bright fringe. Other values of m ($m = 1, 2, 3 \ldots$) indicate fringes to the side of the central bright fringe.

Fringe patterns also result when light passes through more than two slits. The arrangement consisting of a large number of parallel, closely spaced slits is called a diffraction grating. The fringes produced by a grating are sharper and brighter than those produced by a pair of slits. Because the condition for bright fringe formation is the same for both double slits and multiple slits, the equation governing the production of bright fringes by a double slit also applies to a diffraction grating.

Time to Set Up: <1 h
Time in Lab: 1 h
Quantitative Lab

Safety
Students should never look into a direct or reflected laser beam. This experiment should not be set up at eye level. Cardboard can be used to stop the beam after it exits the experimental apparatus.

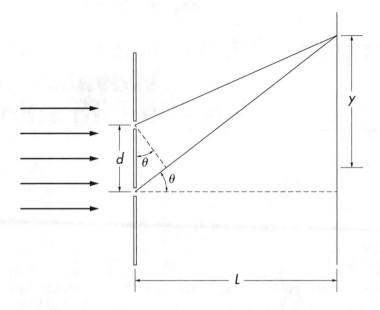

Materials

- diffraction grating
- laser pointers of different colors (red, green, violet)
- four binder clips
- meter stick or tape measure
- white screen (white board or paper)

Procedure

1. Obtain your diffraction grating's slit spacing d from your teacher and record it in the data section below.

2. Use two binder clips to support the laser pointer and two clips to support the diffraction grating.

3. Place the diffraction grating in front of the red laser pointer. The grating should be positioned so that the laser beam passes through the grating perpendicular to its surface.

4. Place the screen on the opposite side of the diffraction grating from the laser.

5. Rotate the laser pointer in the binder clips so that a binder clip holds down the on/off button. An interference pattern should now be visible on the screen.

6. Adjust the distance between the screen and grating until the central and first-order fringes are observed on the screen. The screen should be parallel to the grating's surface.

7. Measure the distance L between the diffraction grating and the screen. Record this distance in the data section.

8. Instruct your lab partner to make marks on the paper at the location of the central bright fringe and the first red fringe ($m = 1$) to the

right of center. Measure the distance between this fringe and the central fringe. Record this as position y_m in Data Table 1.

9. Change the distance between the screen and the grating. Repeat steps 7 and 8. Do this for a total of three different L values.

10. Repeat steps 2—9 using a different color laser pointer and enter the data in Data Table 2.

Data

$d = $ _____m

Data Table 1: Laser 1		
Trial	L (m)	y_m (m)
1		
2		
3		

Data Table 2: Laser 2		
Trial	L (m)	y_m (m)
1		
2		
3		

Table 3 Laser 1				
Trial	tan θ	θ	sin θ	λ (m)
1				
2				
3				

Average wavelength: _____ m

Table 4 Laser 2				
Trial	tan θ	θ	sin θ	λ (m)
1				
2				
3				

Average wavelength: _____ m

Analysis

1. Calculate y_m/L, which is tan θ, for your lasers. Enter these values in Tables 3 and 4.

2. Use your calculator to determine θ for each trial by applying the inverse tangent function. Enter these values in Tables 3 and 4.

3. Use your calculator to determine sin θ for each color. Enter these values in Tables 3 and 4.

4. Use $d \sin θ = mλ$ to find the wavelengths of the laser light. Enter these values in Tables 3 and 4.

5. Calculate the average wavelength for each of your lasers.

Conclusions

1. Ask your teacher for the accepted values for the wavelengths of light produced by the laser pointers. Use these values to determine the percent error in your experimental values.

   _____

   _____

2. Suggest possible sources of error that would lead to discrepancies between accepted and experimental values.

   Errors may arise in the measurement of the distance between the diffraction

   grating and the screen, as well as measurement of the distance between the central

   maximum and the first bright fringe. Error may be introduced by improper alignment

   of diffraction grating and screen.

3. a. With other variables held constant, what effect should increasing L have on the spacing between bright fringes?

   Increasing L will increase the distance between bright fringes.

   b. With other variables held constant, what effect should increasing d have on the space between bright fringes?

   Increasing d will decrease the distance between bright fringes.

4. What would happen to the effective grating spacing if a diffraction grating were rotated about a *vertical* axis through its center? What changes in the interference pattern would be observed as the grating was rotated?

   Rotating the grating would decrease the effective space between slits. This would

   increase the distance between bright fringes.

Chapter 18 Lab   What's My Line?

Your Task

A compact disc is covered with thousands of tightly spaced, nearly parallel lines. These lines are engraved on the disc's surface. In this lab, you must determine the number of lines per centimeter on a compact disc.

Time to Set Up: <1 h
Time in Lab: 1 h
Performance Assessment

Equipment Provided

• Section of a CD-R disc

Cut the CD-R into pie-wedge-shaped pieces. Use tape to remove the foil from the surface of the disc. Give one piece to each group of students.

Requirements

• You must design an experiment to solve the problem.

• You may request additional equipment from your instructor.

• You will submit an equipment list and procedure before taking any data.

• You will only get one chance to ask for equipment. Make sure your list is complete.

• Your procedure should be thorough enough that another student in the class could follow your instructions.

• Present your data in tables, if appropriate.

• Show calculations used to solve the problem, if applicable.

• List at least two sources of error. For each, indicate what effect the error would have on your results.

Materials Desired

Students may ask for a laser with known wavelength, a screen, binder clips,

a protractor, and a meter stick.

_____

_____

_____

_____

Safety
Students should never look into a direct or reflected laser beam. This experiment should not be set up at eye level. Cardboard can be used to stop the beam after it exits the experimental apparatus.

Procedure Followed

Students can shine the laser through the CD and determine the angle to

any maximum they choose. They can find the spacing of the slits using

$d \sin \theta = m\lambda$ and then use the equation $d = 1/N$ to determine the number

of lines per centimeter.

_____

_____

_____

_____

_____

_____

_____

Data Collected

Conclusion

_____

_____

_____

_____

Sources of Error

Possible sources of error include:

- Measurement of the distance between the diffraction grating and the screen
- Measurement of the distance between the central maximum and the first bright fringe
- Improper alignment of diffraction grating and screen

Name _____ Period _____ Date _____

Chapter 19 Lab Exploring Electrostatics

Purpose

In this lab, you will investigate the nature of electric charge, the charging process, and interactions between charges.

Time to Set Up: <1 h
Time in Lab: 1 h
Qualitative Lab

Discussion

Electrostatics is the branch of physics that deals with the properties of and interactions between stationary electric charges. Electrostatic phenomena are so pervasive that it is difficult to name many aspects of the physical world that are not affected by them. Electrical interactions between atoms are responsible for the formation of molecules. On a much grander scale, a rapid discharge of atmospheric electricity manifests itself as a flash of lightning. All these phenomena are governed by the same basic principles.

Materials

Necessary materials will be found at each station.

Procedure

Station 1: Triboelectric Charging

Describe what happens when you try to pick up the bits of paper with the PVC pipe.

Nothing happens when the PVC is uncharged.

Now rub the PVC pipe with wool. Again bring the pipe near the bits of paper as a test. What happens as you approach the pieces of paper?

The paper is attracted to the PVC.

What did the rubbing do to the pipe?

Rubbing charged the pipe.

What happens when you bring the wool near the paper?

After rubbing the wool and PVC, the paper is attracted to the wool, as well.

Try rubbing other combinations of materials together. Try to pick up bits of paper with each of the materials after rubbing them together. Record your observations.

Answers will vary.

Equipment
PVC pipe, wool, bits of paper

Equipment
PVC pipe, electroscope

Station 2: Charging by Contact

Rub the PVC pipe with wool. Bring the pipe in contact with the electroscope. What happens to the electroscope's leaves?

The leaves separate.

Now remove the pipe. Describe the behavior of the leaves when the pipe is withdrawn. Propose an explanation for your observation.

The leaves of the electroscope remain separated. Charge was transferred from the pipe to the electroscope.

Now put the pipe down and touch the top of the electroscope with your finger. What happens to the leaves when you touch the electroscope?

The leaves fall back together.

Why do you think the leaves behave this way?

You ground the electroscope when you touch it, so there is no longer a charge on it.

Equipment
2 X 4 or meter stick, watch glass, PVC pipe, wool

Station 3: Large-Scale Charge Detector

Balance a 2 × 4 board on an inverted watch glass. The watch glass provides a low-friction support for the board. Rub the PVC pipe with wool. Bring the pipe near, but not touching, one side of the board. The closer the pipe is held to the end of the board, the better. What effect does the pipe have on the board?

The board begins to move toward the pipe.

Once the board is in motion, move the pipe to the other side of the board. Does the pipe attract the other side of the board? How do you know?

The pipe attracts the other side of the board. The board slows down and eventually changes direction. There must have been a force on the board in the direction of the pipe to cause this change in the board's motion.

Equipment
PVC pipe, wool, electroscope

Station 4: Charge Polarization

Rub the PVC pipe with wool. Watch the electroscope's leaves as you bring the pipe near (without touching) the top of the electroscope. What do the leaves do as the pipe gets closer?

The leaves of the electroscope separate.

Now move the pipe away from the electroscope. What happens to the leaves as the pipe gets farther away? Explain your observations.

The leaves fall back down to their original position. When the pipe was near the leaves, the charges inside the leaves became polarized. When the pipe was moved away, the charges returned to their original position.

Station 5: Attracting a Neutral Object

Place an aluminum soda can on its side on a table top. Rub the PVC pipe with wool. Bring the pipe, near, but not touching, the can. What happens?

The can rolls toward the PVC pipe.

Explain why this is occurring.

The charged PVC pipe induces a charge polarization on the can. Therefore, the side closest to the pipe is electrically attracted to the pipe.

Once the can is rolling, how can you stop it with the pipe without using your hand?

Place the pipe on the opposite side of the can so that the force it exerts on the can will slow it down.

Equipment
Empty soda can, PVC pipe, wool

Station 6: Deflecting a Stream of Water

Rub the PVC pipe with wool. Bring the PVC pipe near a thin stream of tap water. What happens to the stream as the PVC pipe nears the stream?

The water is attracted to the charged PVC pipe.

Explain your observations.

Due to its atomic structure, water is a polar molecule. The positive sides of water molecules are attracted to the negatively charged pipe.

Equipment
PVC pipe, wool, stream of water (faucet or 2 L bottle with small hole)

Station 7: Combining Electric Forces

You will find three inflated balloons, two of which are untethered and one suspended from a string. Charge the three balloons by rubbing them with wool. Approach the suspended balloon with the other two charged balloons, one in each hand. How does the suspended balloon respond to the approaching balloons? That is, does it move and, if so, in which direction?

The suspended balloon moves away from the student in the forward direction.

Explain the response of the suspended balloon to the two balloons.

The suspended balloon experiences two forces, one from each of the handheld balloons. The one in your right hand pushes the balloon forward and to the left. The one in your left hand pushes the suspended balloon forward and to the right. Therefore, the left and right components cancel, and the net force on the balloon is in the forward direction.

Equipment
Three balloons, string, wool

Assembly
For best results, suspend the balloon from the ceiling.

Equipment
Tape, wire, electroscopes, PVC pipe, wool, string

Station 8: Conductors and Insulators

Use tape to attach the ends of the length of wire to the two electroscopes. Rub the PVC pipe with wool. Touch one of the electroscopes with the PVC pipe. Describe how the electroscopes react.

The leaves of both electroscopes separate.

Propose an explanation for the behavior of the electroscopes.

The wire is a conductor. When charge is placed on one electroscope, the wire allows some of this charge to pass to the other electroscope.

Replace the wire with string and once again touch one electroscope with the PVC pipe. How do the electroscopes behave now?

The leaves of the touched electroscope separate. The leaves of the other electroscope do not.

Explain your observations.

String is not a conductor. Therefore, the charge could not pass through the string and onto the other electroscope.

Chapter 19: Electric Charges and Forces • Tape Electrostatics

Chapter 19 Lab   What's My Charge?

Your Task

In this lab, you must determine the sign of the charge acquired by a piece of tape when it is removed from the table. You will begin by sticking a 15 cm piece of tape to your lab table. You will want to create a handle for your tape by folding the last 1 cm over onto itself. When you tear the tape from the table, it will be charged. It is your job to determine if the tape has acquired a positive or negative charge.

Time to Set Up: <1 h
Time in Lab: 1 h
Performance Assessment

Equipment Provided

• piece of tape

Requirements

• You must design an experiment to solve the problem.

• You may request additional equipment from your instructor.

• You will submit an equipment list and procedure before taking any data.

• You will only get one chance to ask for equipment. Make sure your list is complete.

• Your procedure should be thorough enough that another student in the class could follow your instructions.

• Present your data in tables, if appropriate.

• Show calculations used to solve the problem, if applicable.

• List at least two sources of error. For each, indicate what effect the error would have on your results.

Materials Requested

Students may ask for wool, rods, silk, PVC pipes, and electroscopes.

_____

_____

_____

_____

_____

Procedure Followed

Students can create a charge that they know is either positive or negative. By observing the behavior of the tape when this charge is brought near, they can deduce the charge on the tape.

_____

_____

_____

_____

_____

_____

Data Collected

Encourage the students to do more than one trial. They may want to do a trial with a known negative and positive charge to confirm their results.

Conclusion

_____

_____

_____

_____

Sources of Error

Possible sources of error include:

• Students should do several trials to check the accuracy of their results.

• The students may inadvertently ground the tape if they touch it before they test.

Chapter 20: Electric Fields and Electric Energy • The Nature of the Electric Field

Chapter 20 Lab   Exploring Electric Fields and Electric Energy

Purpose

In this lab, you will explore properties of the electric field, methods of separating charges, and the storage of charge and electric energy.

Materials

Necessary materials will be found at each station.

Discussion

Electric charges produce electric fields that exert forces and store energy. Electric potential energy stored in these fields can be converted to other forms of energy. A device used for charge and energy storage is the capacitor. Consisting of two conducting plates separated by an insulating material, capacitors are found in virtually all electronic devices.

Procedure

Station 1: Charging by Induction

Charge a PVC pipe by rubbing it with wool. Describe the behavior of the electroscope when you bring the pipe near, but not in contact with, the electroscope.

The electroscope leaves spread apart.

With the charged PVC pipe near the electroscope, touch the electroscope with a finger from your free hand. Describe how touching the electroscope affects the leaves.

The leaves collapse.

Remove your finger, keeping the PVC pipe near the electroscope. What happens to the electroscope when your finger is withdrawn?

The leaves remain collapsed.

Now remove the charged PVC pipe. What happens to the electroscope when you remove the pipe?

The leaves spread apart when the pipe is withdrawn.

Time to Set Up: <1 h
Time in Lab: 1 h
Qualitative Lab

Equipment
PVC pipe, wool, electroscope

Why do you think this occurs?

The process results in a net charge on the leaves. The leaves have the same

charge and therefore repel.

How do you think the sign of the charge on the electroscope compares to the sign of the charge on the PVC pipe? How can you test your answer?

The charge on the electroscope and the charge on the pipe are opposites.

This can be shown by bringing a positively charged object near the

electroscope. This will cause the leaves to spread farther apart.

Equipment

Battery holder, two "D" batteries, capacitor (> 2500 μ F), electrical leads, light bulb base with light bulb. These components are often sold together in a kit.

Station 2: Charging on a Capacitor

Place one battery in the battery holder and use leads to connect the holder to the capacitor. Wait 30 seconds to allow the capacitor to fully charge. Disconnect the leads from the battery holder and reconnect them to the light bulb. What happens?

The light bulb lights for a short time.

Place two batteries in the battery holder and repeat the procedure above. What happens?

The light bulb lights for a longer time.

Explain the difference between the two trials.

Using two batteries increases the potential difference, and therefore more

charge is stored on the capacitor.

Equipment

Two cell phones, sheet of aluminum foil, sheet of plastic wrap

Station 3: Shielding

Wrap one cell phone with the plastic wrap. Use the other cell phone to call the wrapped phone. What happens?

The phones are able to connect.

Replace the plastic wrap with the aluminum foil. Call the wrapped phone again. What happens?

The phones are not able to connect.

How do you explain the effects produced by the metal and plastic wrappings?

The metal wrapping shields the phones and does not allow the electromagnetic

waves to penetrate. The electric field inside a closed conductor must be zero.

Station 4: A Charging Device

Rub the Styrofoam plate with wool. Using the Styrofoam cup as a handle, lower the pie tin onto the Styrofoam plate. Touch the pie tin with your finger while it's on the plate. Now pick the pie tin up by the Styrofoam cup handle. What happens when you touch the pie tin to your wrist? You will probably have to pay close attention to notice any effects.

A small spark will be produced.

Repeat the process described above. Does the pie tin once again acquire a charge? How many times do you think you can charge the tin using this process? Try it and see!

The process can be repeated many times. You are the source of the charge, not the Styrofoam.

Equipment
Wool, aluminum pie pan, Styrofoam plate and cup, tape or hot glue

Assembly
Attach the Styrofoam cup to the center of the pie pan using tape or hot glue.

Station 5: Stored Energy

Connect the generator leads to a light bulb. Rotate the handle of the generator. What happens?

The bulb lights as long as the handle is rotated.

Connect the generator to the capacitor. Turn the generator's handle for a minute or two, then quickly disconnect it from the capacitor. Now use two leads to connect the capacitor to the light bulb. What do you observe?

The bulb lights for a short time when the capacitor is connected to it.

Discuss the energy transformations taking place.

The generator converts mechanical energy into stored electric energy in the capacitor. The electric stored energy is converted into radiant energy by the bulb.

Equipment
Hand-cranked electric generator, 1.5- or 2.5-volt light bulb or LED, two electrical leads, 1-farad capacitor

Station 6: The Leyden Jar: An Early Capacitor

The foil-wrapped film canister containing water is a simple charge-storing device called a Leyden jar. Charge the Leyden jar by first rubbing the PVC pipe with wool, then touching the nail at the top of the Leyden jar with the PVC pipe. How can you test the Leyden jar for charge?

Touch the Leyden jar's nail to your wrist.

What effect does repeating the charging process several times have on the charge stored? Try it and see!

The charge stored in the Leyden jar increases each time the PVC pipe touches the nail.

Equipment
Aluminum foil, plastic or glass container with lid (e.g., 35 mm film canister), small nail, water, PVC pipe, wool

Assembly
Tape strips of aluminum foil around the outside and inside bottom third of the container. Poke the nail through the container's lid. Fill the container half full with water.

Equipment
Metal cup, conducting ball on an insulated handle, electroscope, PVC pipe, wool, Styrofoam platform

Station 7: Location of Charge on a Conductor
Place the metal cup on the Styrofoam platform. Charge the cup by touching it with the charged PVC pipe. Holding the insulating handle, touch the conducting ball to the lower inside of the cup. Be sure to touch only the inside of the cup. Then touch the ball to the electroscope. What happens to the electroscope? What does this tell you about the inside of the cup?

The leaves of the electroscope do not separate. The inside of the cup is

uncharged.

Holding the insulating handle, touch the conducting ball to the outside of the cup. Then touch the ball to the electroscope. What happens to the electroscope? What does this tell you about the outside of the cup?

The leaves separate. The outside of the cup is charged.

What does this activity tell you about the location of charge on a conductor?

Charge resides only on the outside surface of a conductor.

Equipment
Commercially available plasma ball, 10 cm square of aluminum foil mounted on cardboard, multimeter, electrical lead with alligator clip on one end, dowel rod

Assembly
Use tape or glue to attach the foil to the cardboard. Attach the lead to the foil with an alligator clip. Attach the other end of the lead to the positive terminal of the multimeter. For best results, attach the foil-covered card to a dowel rod or other insulator and set the multimeter to the millivolt range.

Station 8: Electric Field Surrounding Plasma Ball
Turn on the multimeter and set it to the millivolt range. While holding the insulating rod, bring the aluminum foil close and parallel to the surface of the plasma ball. Describe the reading on the meter.

The meter should read several millivolts. The reading will depend on the

plasma ball used.

What does the meter reading tell you about the space surrounding the plasma ball?

There is an electric field in the space surrounding the plasma ball.

Move the foil away from the plasma ball. Describe the meter reading at various distances from the plasma ball.

The meter reading will decrease with distance.

Chapter 20: Electric Fields and Electric Energy • Parallel Plate Capacitor

Chapter 20 Lab   Properties of a Parallel Plate Capacitor

Purpose

In this lab, you will investigate how the capacitance of a parallel plate capacitor is related to plate separation and surface area of the two plates.

Time to Set Up: <1 h
Time in Lab: 1 h
Quantitative Lab

Discussion

Consisting of two conductors separated by a nonconducting medium, capacitors are electrical devices used to store electric charge and electric energy. When the conductors are connected to the terminals of a source of potential difference, such as a battery, one conductor acquires a positive charge and the other conductor acquires an equal negative charge. Composed of two metal parallel plates separated by an insulating material, a parallel plate capacitor is the simplest to construct and analyze.

Materials

- aluminum foil
- capacitance meter
- electrical leads
- meter stick
- textbook

Inexpensive capacitance meters capable of measuring pF are available from a variety of Internet vendors.

Procedure

Part A: Dependence of Capacitance on Separation of Parallel Plates

1. Prepare two sheets of aluminum foil to serve as plates. The two plates should have the same dimensions and be a little smaller than the size of a page in your textbook.

2. Cut two aluminum foil strips approximately 2 cm wide $\times$ 10 cm long. Fold them in half to form 5-cm-long strips of double thickness. Use adhesive tape to attach a 5 cm strip to each plate. The attached strips should be offset so that they will not touch when the plates are inserted in the textbook.

3. Insert the plates in the textbook with 25 pages between sheets. Make certain that the two plates are in alignment.

4. Close the book and press down on it to ensure that the pages are close together.

5. Set the multimeter to the picofarad (pF) range.

6. After inserting two leads into the meter, turn on the multimeter.

7. Zero the multimeter.

8. Attach the multimeter's two leads to the strips on the foil plates.

9. After the meter becomes stable, read the capacitance and record it in Data Table 1.

10. Repeat steps 3–9, each time increasing the number of pages between the plates in steps, as indicated in Data Table 1.

Part B: Dependence of Capacitance on Area of Parallel Plates

1. Find the capacitance for a plate separation of 100 pages in Data Table 1. Enter this capacitance under the Capacitance heading on the "Full plate" line in Data Table 2.

2. Repeat steps 3–9 as outlined in Part A, keeping a plate separation of 100 pages but varying the area of the plates by folding the plates in half. Enter the capacitance after one fold on the "One-half plate" line in Data Table 2.

3. Determine the capacitance after a second fold and enter the result on the "One-quarter plate" line.

4. Continue folding the plates and measuring the capacitance until the area of the plates reaches one-sixteenth of the original size.

You may wish to have students produce single-thickness plates by using scissors to cut along the fold lines.

Data

Data Table 1		
Trial	Plate separation (number of pages)	Capacitance (pF)
1	25	
2	50	
3	75	
4	100	
5	125	
6	150	

Data Table 2	
Plate surface area	Capacitance (pF)
Full plate	
One-half plate	
One-quarter plate	
One-eighth plate	
One-sixteenth plate	

Analysis

1. Produce a graph of capacitance versus plate separation.
2. Produce a graph of capacitance versus plate surface area.

Using Excel will allow students to find the functional relationship between capacitance and plate separation.

Conclusions

1. Describe the relationship between capacitance and plate separation for a parallel plate capacitor.

   The capacitance is inversely related to plate separation.

2. Describe the relationship between capacitance and plate surface area for a parallel plate capacitor.

   The capacitance is directly related to the plate surface area.

3. How would the capacitance of a parallel capacitor change if both the distance between plates and the area of the plates were doubled?

   The capacitance would not be affected.

4. How would the capacitance of a parallel plate capacitor change if the distance between the plates were halved and the area of the plates were doubled?

   The capacitance would increase fourfold.

Chapter 21: Electric Current and Electric Circuits • Simple Electric Circuits

Chapter 21 Lab   Exploring Simple Electric Circuits

Purpose

In this lab, you will construct electric circuits containing batteries, bulbs, and wire using different types of circuit arrangements.

Time to Set Up: <1 h
Time in Lab: 1 h
Qualitative Lab

Discussion

An electric circuit is a path along which electric charge is able to flow. A simple circuit might consist of an electric cell (a source of potential difference, such as a flashlight battery), conducting wires, and a load, such as a small lamp.

Electric circuits are found everywhere you turn: in MP3 players, automobiles, computers, and the human body. They range in size from the smallest, consisting of just two wires separated by about 150 atoms, to the largest, the U.S. electric grid, a network of cables that carries electric energy to consumers all across the nation. The complexity of circuits also runs the gamut from simple circuits in flashlights to the amazingly intricate collection of neural pathways found in the brain. Although conductors can be assembled in countless ways, many of them are simply combinations of series and parallel arrangements.

Materials

• six connecting wires with alligator clips
• four miniature 2.5 V bulbs
• four bulb sockets
• two "D" batteries, one single D battery holder

Procedure

1. Arrange one bulb (not in a socket), one battery, and one wire in as many ways as you can to make the bulb light. Sketch each arrangement that resulted in the bulb's lighting. Describe the similarities of your successful trials.

All the arrangements involve a complete path from the battery through the bulb and back to the opposite pole of the battery.

2. Try to light a bulb using only the battery and no wire. Describe your results.

This cannot be done.

3. Using one battery and one wire, light as many bulbs (not in sockets) as you can. Sketch the arrangements that resulted in all the bulbs' lighting. You may need your lab partner to help with this.

4. Symbols that may be used to represent batteries, bulbs, and wires are shown below.

Bulb   Cell   Wire

5. Connect the bulbs (in sockets), battery, and wires as shown in the circuit diagram below. This represents a series circuit.

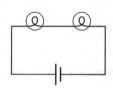

6. Note the brightness of the bulbs in the circuit above. Describe the brightness of each bulb.

The bulbs are equally bright.

7. Add a third bulb and socket to the circuit above to create a three-bulb series circuit. Sketch the circuit diagram below.

8. Do the bulbs light in each of these series circuits? If so, compare the brightness of the bulbs in the circuit containing two bulbs versus the one containing three bulbs.

The bulbs in the two-bulb circuit are brighter.

9. Remove one bulb from the series circuit containing three bulbs. What happens to the other bulbs?

   All the bulbs go out.

10. Construct the circuit shown in the diagram below. This represents a parallel circuit. Note the brightness of the bulbs in this circuit.

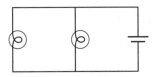

11. Now add a third bulb in parallel. Note the brightness of the bulbs in this circuit. Sketch the circuit diagram below.

12. Do all the bulbs light in each of these parallel circuits? If so, compare the brightness of the bulbs in the circuit containing two bulbs to the brightness in the one containing three bulbs.

   All the bulbs are equally bright

13. Remove one bulb from the parallel circuit containing three bulbs. What happens to the other bulbs?

   The remaining bulbs stay lit.

14. Remove the battery from the holder. Examine the markings on the top and bottom sides of a D battery. You should see a + at the top and a — at the bottom of the cell. These symbols represent the positive and negative terminals of the cell.

15. Line up two batteries so that the positive terminal of one battery is touching the negative terminal of the other. With this arrangement of batteries, use as many pieces of wire as necessary to get one bulb to light. How does the brightness of the bulb connected to two batteries compare to the brightness of a bulb connected to a single battery?

   The bulbs are brighter when connected to two batteries.

16. Repeat step 15, but with the positive terminals of the two batteries touching each other. Describe the brightness of the bulb when the batteries are in this arrangement.

   The bulbs do not light.

Analysis and Conclusions

1. What requirements must be met in order for a light bulb to light?

   There must be a complete path, a source of potential difference, and conducting wires.

2. Summarize the differences between series and parallel circuits.

   In a series circuit, there is a single path for the current. If one bulb is removed, all

   bulbs go out. All bulbs are equally bright, and adding bulbs reduces the brightness

   of the bulbs. In a parallel circuit, there are multiple paths for the current. All bulbs are

   equally bright regardless of the number of bulbs. Removing one bulb does not affect

   the remaining bulbs.

3. What types of circuits are used in household wiring? Support your answer.

   Household wiring is in parallel. When one appliance is unplugged, the remaining

   appliances can still operate.

4. Many years ago, if one light bulb in a string of holiday lights burned out, all the
   light bulbs would go out. What type of circuit was used to connect the light bulbs
   in these old strings of lights? Explain your reasoning.

   The bulbs were connected in a series circuit. If they had been in parallel, the

   remaining bulbs would have stayed lit when a single bulb burned out.

5. The brightness of a light bulb is related to the power it consumes. Which type
   of circuit, series or parallel, containing three light bulbs consumes more power?
   Explain your answer.

   The parallel circuit contains the brighter bulbs, and therefore it consumes more

   power.

Chapter 21: Electric Current and Electric Circuits • Resistance and Resistivity

Chapter 21 Lab   Resistance and Resistivity of Modeling Dough

Purpose

In this lab, you will investigate the dependence of electric resistance on the length and cross-sectional area of a conductor.

Time to Set Up: <1 h
Time in Lab: 1 h
Quantitative Lab

Materials 🖐️

• one 5 oz. can of children's electrically conductive modeling dough

• two multimeters

• variable power supply

• three connecting wires with alligator clips

• two voltmeter leads with pointed probes at one end

• two short nails

• small ruler

• tape

Examples of electrically conducting dough include RoseArt Fun Dough® and Play-Doh®.

Discussion

Electric resistance represents an object's opposition to the flow of electric charge and is defined by the relationship $R = V/I$, where R is the resistance, V is the voltage, and I is the current. The electric resistance of an object depends on several factors, including geometry—that is, length and cross-sectional area—and the nature of the material from which the object is made. The resistivity of a substance ρ is defined as RA/L, where R is the resistance, A is the cross-sectional area, and L is the length. Unlike resistance, resistivity is an intrinsic property of a material and does not depend on the geometry of a particular sample.

Procedure

Part A: Dependence of Resistance on Length

1. Remove approximately one-third of the dough from the can. Knead dough to remove cracks and gaps.

2. Using a portion of the dough, fashion a cylinder 10 cm long and 1 cm in diameter. Make the diameter of the cylinder as uniform as possible. Return excess dough to the can to prevent dough from drying out.

3. Insert the two nails into the ends of the cylinder to a depth of approximately 1 cm.

4. Use a small centimeter ruler and pencil tip to make shallow marks at 1 cm intervals along the length of the cylinder.

5. Use the alligator clips to attach two of the connecting wires to the nails. Taping the wires to the table top will prevent the nails from moving around inside the cylinder.

6. Use the remaining connecting wire to construct a series circuit consisting of the power supply, one multimeter, and the cylinder (see figure below).

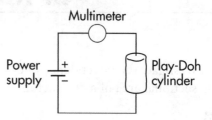

7. Set the multimeter in the circuit on the 100 mA scale.

8. Turn on the power supply and adjust the voltage until the multimeter reads 10 mA. Turn off the power supply once a 10 mA current has been achieved.

9. After setting the second multimeter to the 10 V range, insert the meter's pointed probes into the cylinder at points 1 cm from each end. The tips of the probes should penetrate the cylinder to a depth of only 1 or 2 mm. This means that the length of the dough between the probes is 8 cm.

10. Have your lab partner turn on the power supply and simultaneously read the voltage between probes and the current through the cylinder, as displayed on the two multimeters. Record voltage and current in Data Table 1. The power supply should be turned off immediately after taking readings.

11. Use the markings on the dough to shorten the length of the dough between the probes to 7 cm. Turn on the power supply again. Record the current and voltage values in Data Table 1.

12. Continue to read and record the voltage and current as you reduce the length of the dough between the probes in steps of 1 cm, stopping at a separation of 1 cm.

The power supply must be turned off between trials, because if left on it will change the composition of the dough.

Part B: Dependence of Resistance on Cross-Sectional Area

1. Use the dough from the cylinder in Part A to create a new cylinder with a length of 10 cm but with a different diameter. Depending on the diameter selected, you may have to use additional dough from the can. Measure the diameter of the dough cylinder and record this value in Data Table 2.

2. Insert the two nails into the ends of the cylinder to a depth of approximately 1 cm.

3. Use a small centimeter ruler and pencil tip to make shallow marks that are 7 cm apart.

4. Using connecting wires, complete the circuit shown in the Part A figure above. Remember to use tape to keep the wires attached to the nails from moving.

5. Set the multimeter in the circuit on the 100 mA scale.

6. After setting the second multimeter to the 10 V range, insert the multimeter probes in the dough so that there is 7 cm of dough between them. The tips of the probes should penetrate the cylinder to a depth of only 1 or 2 mm.

7. Have your lab partner turn on the power supply and simultaneously read the voltage between probes and the current through the cylinder as displayed on the two multimeters. Record voltage and current in Data Table 2. The power supply should be turned off immediately after taking readings.

8. Repeat steps 1—7 six times, each time using a cylinder with a length of 10 cm but with a different diameter.

Different colors of dough have different resistivities. You may want to have students investigate the resistance and resistivity of dough of a different color as an extension activity.

Data

Cylinder diameter: 1 cm

Data Table 1			
Trial	Distance between probes (m)	Voltage (V)	Current (A)
1			
2			
3			
4			
5			
6			
7			
8			

Distance between probes: 7 cm

Data Table 2			
Sample	Cylinder diameter (m)	Voltage (V)	Current (A)
1			
2			
3			
4			
5			
6			
7			

Analysis

1. Use the data in Data Table 1 to complete Table 3. *Note:* The cross-sectional area of a cylinder A equals $\pi(d/2)^2$, where d is the diameter of the cylinder, the resistance R equals V/I, and the resistivity $\rho = RA/L$.

2. Use the data in Data Table 2 to complete Table 4.

3. Construct a graph of resistance versus length (the distance between probes) based on the data in Table 3.

4. Construct a graph of resistance versus cross-sectional area based on the data in Table 4.

Table 3				
Trial	Distance between probes (m)	Cross-sectional area of cylinder (m²)	Resistance (Ω)	Resistivity (Ω m)
1				
2				
3				
4				
5				
6				
7				
8				

Table 4			
Trial	Distance between probes (m)	Cross-sectional area of cylinder (m²)	Resistance (Ω)
1			
2			
3			
4			
5			
6			
7			

Conclusions

1. Based on the graph of resistance versus length, what relationship exists between resistance and length?

   Length and resistance are directly related. The graph is a straight line.

2. What happened to the resistance in Part A of the experiment as the distance between voltmeter probes was decreased? Why do you think this happened?

   The resistance decreased. There was less material between the probes.

3. Based on the graph of resistance versus cross-sectional area, what relationship exists between resistance and cross-sectional area?

   Area and resistance are inversely related. The graph shows an inverse relationship.

4. What effect did increasing the cylinder diameter have on the resistance in Part B of the experiment? Why do you think this happened?

   Increasing the diameter decreased the resistance. Increasing the diameter increases

   the number of charge carriers in a cross-section of the conductor.

5. Was the resistivity of the dough constant or does it depend on the of length or cross-sectional area of the sample?

   The resistivity of the dough should remain constant.

6. Summarize the factors that affect the resistance of a conductor.

   The length and cross-sectional area affect the resistance of a conductor. Resistance may

   also depend on the color of the dough used (i.e., on the composition of the dough).

Chapter 21: Electric Current and Electric Circuits • **Series and Parallel Circuits**

Chapter 21 Lab   Series and Parallel Resistor Circuits

Purpose

In this lab, you will discover how the type of circuit (series or parallel) affects the total resistance of the circuit and the potential difference across the individual resistors.

Discussion

Ohm's law states that the current in a circuit is directly proportional to the potential difference and inversely proportional to the resistance. When there is more than one resistor in a circuit, the resistors can be arranged in series, in parallel, or in some combination of series and parallel. In a series circuit, there is only one path for the current. In a parallel circuit, there are multiple paths for the current.

Materials

- three resistors of known resistance
- "D" batteries
- battery holder
- multimeter

Procedure

1. Create a simple circuit consisting of the battery holder and one resistor. Use the multimeter to measure the current between the battery and the resistor and the voltage across the battery. Also, measure the current through and the voltage across the resistor. Record these values in Data Table 1.

2. Add another resistor to your circuit so that there is only one path for the current to take to go back to the battery. This is a series circuit. Record the current through each resistor and the voltage across each resistor. Also measure the current between the battery and the first resistor and the voltage across the battery. Record these values in Data Table 2.

3. Add a third resistor in series and measure the values as you did in step 2. Record these values in Data Table 3.

4. Return to the simple circuit from step 1. Add a second resistor in parallel. That is, make another path from one terminal of the battery to the other with this new resistor.

5. Following the procedure used in the previous trials, measure the voltage and current for each resistor and the battery. Record these values in Data Table 4.

Time to Set Up: <1 h
Time in Lab: 1 h
Quantitative Lab

Depending on the resistors and multimeter used, you may need to use more than one battery. Instruct students on the proper use of the multimeter.

6. Add a third resistor in parallel and measure as before. Record these values in Data Table 5.

Data

Data Table 1		
	V (V)	I (A)
Battery		
Resistor 1		

Data Table 2		
	V (V)	I (A)
Battery		
Resistor 1		
Resistor 2		

Data Table 3		
	V (V)	I (A)
Battery		
Resistor 1		
Resistor 2		
Resistor 3		

Data Table 4		
	V (V)	I (A)
Battery		
Resistor 1		
Resistor 2		

Data Table 5		
	V (V)	I (A)
Battery		
Resistor 1		
Resistor 2		
Resistor 3		

Analysis

1. Using symbols, draw a circuit diagram for each of the five circuits you created.

2. In which trials were the resistors connected in series?

The resistors were connected in series for trials 2 and 3

3. In which trials were the resistors connected in parallel?

The resistors were connected in parallel for trials 4 and 5.

4. For the series circuits, what happened to the current in the circuit as you added more resistors? What does this suggest about the total resistance in the circuit?

As you add more resistors, the current decreases. This indicates that the total

resistance is increasing.

5. For a series circuit, how do the currents through each of the resistors compare?

In a series circuit all, the resistors have the same current.

6. For Data Tables 1, 2, and 3 add the voltage drop across each resistor to find the total voltage drop for the circuit. How do these numbers compare?

The total voltage drop of the circuit should be the same for each trial.

7. For the parallel circuits, what happens to the current that is drawn from the battery as you add more resistors in parallel? What does this suggest about the total resistance of the circuit?

As more resistors are added in parallel, the current drawn from the battery increases.

This suggests that the total resistance of the circuit is reduced.

8. What can you say about the voltage across resistors connected in parallel?

When resistors are connected in parallel, the voltage across all the resistors is the same.

Chapter 21: Electric Current and Electric Circuits • Applying Ohm's Law

Chapter 21 Lab   How Long Is the Wire?

Your Task

In this lab, you must determine the length of a coil of copper wire.

Equipment Provided

- length of insulated copper wire

Requirements

- You must design an experiment to solve the problem.
- You may request additional equipment from your instructor.
- You will submit an equipment list and procedure before taking any data.
- You will only get one chance to ask for equipment. Make sure your list is complete.
- Your procedure should be thorough enough that another student in the class could follow your instructions.
- Present your data in tables, if appropriate.
- Show calculations used to solve the problem, if applicable.
- List at least two sources of error. For each, indicate what effect the error would have on your results.

Materials Requested

Students may ask for a power supply or battery, resistors, caliper or

micrometer, and multimeter.

_____

_____

_____

_____

Procedure Followed

Students can find the resistance of the wire by connecting it to a known

voltage, measuring the current, and using Ohm's law. They can use the

caliper to measure the radius of the wire and determine the cross-sectional

area. The resistivity of copper is about 1.7×10^{-8} Ωm. They can use the

equation $R = \rho L/A$ to determine the length of the coiled wire. Have students

untie and measure the actual length of the wire to check their answer.

Time to Set Up: <1 h
Time in Lab: 1 h
Performance Assessment

Give each group of students a length (3–10 feet) of insulated copper wire that is tied in a tight coil. The wire should be thick enough so that they can estimate the cross-sectional area of the wire.

_____
_____
_____
_____

Data

Conclusion

_____
_____
_____
_____

Sources of Error

Possible sources of error include::
_____

• Students may have difficulty measuring the diameter of the copper wire.

• The resistance of the copper may change as it heats up.

• The resistivity of copper falls in a range from 16.7 to 17.2 nΩm.

Chapter 21: Electric Current and Electric Circuits • **Battery Resistance**

Chapter 21 Lab   Internal Resistance

Your Task

In this lab, you must determine the internal resistance of a battery.

Time to Set Up: <1 h
Time in Lab: 1 h
Performance Assessment

Equipment Provided 🗲

• a "C" or "D" battery

Requirements

• You must design an experiment to solve the problem.

• You may request additional equipment from your instructor.

• You will submit an equipment list and procedure before taking any data.

• You will only get one chance to ask for equipment. Make sure your list is complete.

• Your procedure should be thorough enough that another student in the class could follow your instructions.

• Present your data in tables, if appropriate.

• Show calculations used to solve the problem, if applicable.

• List at least two sources of error. For each, indicate what effect the error would have on your results.

Materials Requested

Students may ask for a light bulb or resistors, connecting wires, and a

multimeter.

_____

_____

_____

_____

_____

Procedure Followed

Students can find the resistance of the battery by creating a circuit with

a single resistor. Students use the multimeter to measure the current in

the circuit and the voltage drop across the known resistor and the voltage

across the terminals of the battery. Using these values, they can determine

the amount of resistance that must exist in the battery.

_____

_____

_____

_____

_____

Data

Conclusion

_____

_____

_____

_____

Sources of Error

Possible sources of error include:

• The total resistance in the circuit also includes the resistance of the wires.

_____

_____

Chapter 22 Lab   Exploring Magnetism and Magnetic Fields

Purpose

In this lab, you will explore magnetism and its sources, interactions between magnets and magnetic fields, and the nature of magnetic materials.

Time to Set Up: <1 h
Time in Lab: <1 h
Qualitative Lab

Discussion

Prior to the 19th century, scientists believed that electricity and magnetism were distinct phenomena, even though the two shared some common characteristics. It is now known that electricity and magnetism are simply different aspects of the unified field of electromagnetism.

Moving charge is responsible for all magnetic effects. Charges moving through a wire or empty space produce a magnetic field, a region surrounding a magnet capable of exerting a force on another magnet. At the atomic level, orbiting electrons are responsible for magnetism. A region within a magnetic material where atomic electrons are aligned in the same direction is referred to as a **magnetic domain**. When an external field is applied to certain materials, the magnetic domains that are pointing in the direction of the applied field tend to grow in size. This may result in the material's becoming a permanent magnet.

Materials

Necessary materials will be found at each station.

Procedure

Station 1: Magnetic Interactions

Describe what happens when you move the north pole of one bar magnet close to the south pole of another bar magnet.?

The poles attract.
_____

Move the north pole of one bar magnet close to the north pole of another bar magnet. Describe what happens now.

The poles repel.
_____

Move the south pole of one bar magnet close to the south pole of another bar magnet. Describe what happens now.

The poles repel.
_____

Equipment
Two bar magnets

Summarize your observations regarding the interactions between the poles of the magnets.

Opposite poles attract and like poles repel.

Equipment
Five ceramic ring magnets, pencil

Station 2: Magnetic Repulsion
Place five ceramic ring magnets on a vertically held pencil. The magnets should be arranged so that they levitate above one another. Push down on the top magnet to compress the vertical array of magnets. Now remove your finger from the top magnet. Describe what happens when the magnets are released.

The magnets spring apart.

What effect does distance have on the strength of the magnetic force?

The force of repulsion increases as the distance between magnets decreases.

Equipment
Dollar bill, neodymium magnet

Station 3: Picking Up Some Cash
Hold one end of a dollar bill in your hand with the length of the bill perpendicular to the table top. Watch closely as you bring a neodymium magnet very close to the free end of the bill. What do you observe?

The strong magnet attracts the ferromagnetic materials in the inks used in

paper currency.

Now bring the magnet's other pole close to the end of the bill. What happens this time? Explain your observations.

The magnet still attracts the bill. Magnetic domains within the ink rearrange

themselves in such a way so as to remain attracted to the magnet.

Equipment
Bar magnet, iron filings, sheet of glass or plastic

Station 4: Mapping Magnetic Fields
Place a sheet of glass or clear plastic over a bar magnet. Sprinkle iron filings onto the sheet above the magnet. Gently tap the glass or plastic. What happens?

The filings arrange themselves in such a way as to reveal the magnetic field

surrounding the magnet.

Make a sketch of the pattern produced by the iron filings.

View the effect of two bar magnets on the filings when the magnets' opposite poles are facing each other and are separated by a distance of a few centimeters. Make a sketch of the pattern produced by the iron filings.

Station 5: Source of the Magnetic Field

Place the wire over the compass so that the wire is above and parallel to the compass needle. Briefly connect and then disconnect the ends of the wire to the terminals of the battery. What happens?

The compass needle aligns itself perpendicular to the wire.

_____

_____

_____

_____

What does the current in the wire produce?

The current produces a magnetic field.

Reverse the battery so that the end of the wire that was touching the positive terminal now touches the negative terminal, and vice versa. Once again, briefly touch the ends of the wire to the battery terminals. What happens? Why do you think this occurs?

The needle still aligns itself perpendicular to the wire, but now points in the

opposite direction.

Equipment
Compass, wire, battery

Station 6: Magnetic Field around a Current-Carrying Wire 🏃

Place the compasses on the sheet in a circle around the wire. They should be equally spaced and positioned at a distance of 3 or 4 cm from the wire. Turn on the power supply and increase the current until the compasses begin to respond. Quickly observe the orientation of the compass needles, then turn off the power supply. Make a sketch showing the direction of the compass needles with respect to the wire.

Reverse the direction of the current in the wire by reversing the wire's connections to the power supply. Once again, turn on the power supply and increase the current until the compasses move. Make a

Equipment
Six small compasses, length of wire, power supply, two electrical leads, cardboard, three rings, ringstand

Assembly
Make a small hole in a square of cardboard. Pass a length of wire through the hole. Arrange three rings on a ringstand so that they are equally spaced. Support the cardboard on the center ring. Stretch the wire between and anchor its ends to the remaining rings. Connect the two electrical leads to the power supply and the ends of the stretched wire.

sketch showing the direction of the compass needles with respect to the wire.

What effect did reversing the current have on the direction of the magnetic field?

Reversing the direction of the current caused the compass needles to reverse direction.

Station 7: Force on a Current-Carrying Wire

Equipment
Horseshoe magnet, length of wire, power supply

Place the wire between the poles of the horseshoe magnet. Simultaneously touch the ends of the wire to the terminals of the power supply. What happens?

The wire will move either up or down, depending on the direction of the current in the wire.

Why do you think this occurs?

A current in a magnetic field will experience a force.

Reverse the battery so that the end of the wire that was touching the positive terminal now touches the negative terminal, and vice versa. Once again, briefly touch the ends of the wire to the battery terminals. How does the wire behave now?

It will once again move, but in a direction opposite to its previous motion.

Explain any changes you observed in the behavior of the wire.

The motion of the wire depends on the direction of the current and the direction of the disks' magnetic field.

Equipment
Iron nail, 1 meter of 22-gauge insulated copper wire, variable power supply, four connecting wires with alligator clips, voltmeter, paper clips, drinking straw

Assembly
Insert the nail in the straw. Wrap 40 turns of wire around the straw, leaving some wire free at each end. Use connecting wires to connect the ends of copper wire and the voltmeter leads in parallel to the power supply.

Station 8: Strength of an Electromagnet

With the nail removed from the wire and straw assembly, set the power supply output to 1 volt. After turning on the power supply, bring the coil to within a centimeter above the paper clips. How many paper clips did the coil pick up? (Turn off the power supply immediately after picking up the paper clips.)

Very few, if any, paper clips will be picked up by the coil of wire.

Make an electromagnet by reinserting the nail in the wire and straw assembly. Turn on the power supply, and once again position the tip of the nail near the paper clips. Compare the strength of the electromagnetic field with that of the coil alone.

The electromagnet is much stronger with the nail in place.

With the nail in the straw, increase the voltage in increments of 1 volt for four more trials. Record the number of paper clips that are picked up for each voltage.

Answers will vary.

What effect does the voltage have on the ability of the electromagnet to pick up paper clips?

The higher the voltage, the greater the number of paper clips picked up by

the electromagnet.

Station 9: Hearing Shifting Magnetic Domains

Connect the telephone pickup to the amplifier. Turn on the amplifier. Listen carefully as you move a magnet toward the telephone pickup. Do you hear a hissing sound? What do you think might be producing the sound?

Shifting magnetic domains induce an emf and an accompanying current in

the iron core.

Move the magnet away from the telephone pickup. What do you hear now?

A hissing sound is heard.

Equipment
Telephone pickup or coil of wire with iron core, amplifier, speaker, magnet

Chapter 22 Lab   Magnetic Force on a Current-Carrying Wire

Purpose

In this lab, you will determine how the force on a wire in a magnet field varies with the current and length of the wire.

Discussion

When a charged particle moves through a magnetic field, the particle experiences a magnetic force. The magnetic force is perpendicular to both the velocity of the charge and the direction of the magnetic field. Because a current consists of moving charges, it follows that a current-carrying wire will also experience such a force. By measuring the force exerted on a current-carrying wire due to an external magnetic field, the relationship between the force on the wire, the current in the wire, and the length of the wire can be determined. Knowledge of these three quantities will, in turn, allow determination of the magnetic field. In this experiment, the magnetic field will be produced by a permanent magnet. The force on a current-carrying wire will be determined by observing the force exerted by a wire on the magnet sitting on a scale.

Materials

- battery holder
- three batteries
- electrical leads
- resistor board
- digital electronic scale
- magnet channel
- multimeter
- wire stirrups

Time to Set Up: <1 h
Time in Lab: 1 h
Quantitative Lab

This equipment can be purchased as a set or made using instructions found in the article "Apparatus for teaching physics: Measuring the magnetic force on a current-carrying conductor," W. Herreman and R. Huysentruyt, *Phys. Teach.* 33, 288 (1995).

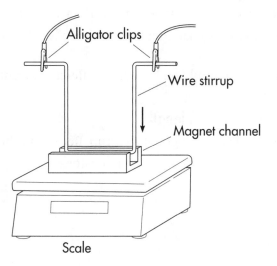

Alligator clips

Wire stirrup

Magnet channel

Scale

Procedure

It is best if your scale reads to the centigram.

1. Place the magnet on the balance.

2. Turn on the multimeter and make sure it is set up to measure current up to 10 A.

3. Place three batteries in the battery holder. Connect a series circuit that includes the battery holder, resistor board, multimeter, and stirrup. Check the multimeter to see if there is a current in the loop. Disconnect the circuit.

4. Draw this circuit in your notebook. Make sure to indicate the $+/-$ poles of the batteries and indicate the direction of the current on your diagram.

5. Zero the scale with the magnet channel on it.

6. Connect the circuit again. Hold the stirrup with the paper handle and carefully lower it into the magnet channel. Make sure that the stirrup does not touch the sides or bottom of the channel.

7. Hold the stirrup still while in the channel and note the reading on the scale. Record this value in Data Table 1.

8. Remove the stirrup from the channel and disconnect the circuit.

Although it is possible to use ringstands to hold the stirrups, the lab works well when students hold them.

9. Reverse the leads that attach to the battery and repeat steps 5–8.

How does force vary with current?

10. The resistor board has four resistors that are connected in series. You can increase the resistance in the circuit by changing the location of the electrical leads on the board.

11. Reconnect the circuit so that the scale readings will be positive.

12. Pick any stirrup and measure the horizontal length of it that will be in the magnet channel.

13. Zero the scale, if necessary.

14. Hold the stirrup in the channel so that it does not touch the channel.

15. Record the current and scale reading in Data Table 2.

16. Adjust the current by changing the location of the leads on the resistor board.

17. Repeat steps 13–16 until you have four different current and scale measurements.

How does force vary with length?

18. Measure the horizontal length of a stirrup. Record this in Data Table 3.

19. Reconnect the circuit using only one resistor.

20. Place the stirrup in the channel as before. Record the current and scale reading in Data Table 3.
21. Repeat steps 17–20 for three other stirrups of different lengths.

Data

Circuit Diagram

Data Table 1	
	Scale reading (g)
Trial 1	
Trial 2	

Data Table 2: Length of Stirrup: _____ m				
Trial	Current (A)	Scale reading (g)	Force (N)	Magnetic field (T)
1				
2				
3				
4				

Data Table 3				
Length of wire (m)	Current (A)	Scale reading (g)	Force (N)	Magnetic field (T)

Analysis and Conclusions

1. Explain any differences in the values you obtained for the scale reading in Data Table 1.

   In one case the scale reading is positive, and in the other it is negative. When the direction of the current changes, the direction of the magnetic force also changes.

2. The scale reading is an indication of the force between the magnet and the wire. Determine the magnitude of the forces for all the trials for Data Tables 2 and 3.

3. Use your data from Data Table 2 to create a graph of force versus current.

4. What does the graph you created in step 3 tell you about the relationship between force and current?

The current and force are directly related.

_____

5. Use your data from Data Table 3 to create a graph of force versus length.

6. What does the graph you created in step 5 tell you about the relationship between force and length?

The length and the force are directly related.

_____

7. Use the equation for the force on a current-carrying wire, $F = BIL$, to determine the magnitude of the magnetic field created by the magnets in the channel for all your trials in Data Tables 2 and 3.

8. Obtain the unknown stirrup from your instructor. Determine the length of this stirrup indirectly using the magnetic force it experiences. Show your data and calculations.

Student answers will vary. They should use the B-field strength they calculated in

step 7 above.

9. Measure the length of the stirrup directly. Determine your percent error in the calculated length from step 8. Actual length = _____m

_____

_____

Chapter 23 Lab Exploring Electromagnetic Induction

Purpose

In this lab, you will observe electric currents induced by changing magnetic fields and examine the effect of induced eddy currents in conductors. In addition, you will observe the relationship between electric generators and motors.

Discussion

In 1820, Danish scientist Hans Christian Oersted made a remarkable discovery. He found that an electric current affects a magnetic compass. Later, Michael Faraday observed that moving a magnet through a coil of wire produced an electric current. There was clearly a link between electricity and magnetism, but what was it?

It was James Clerk Maxwell who clarified the connection. In 1865, he published a landmark paper describing electricity and magnetism as different aspects of a unifying phenomenon called electromagnetism.

The discoveries relating to electromagnetism ushered in a whole new technology. Oersted's discovery ultimately led to the electric motor, Faraday's to the electric generator. Working in concert, the motor and generator introduced the widespread use and production of electric energy and with them an improved standard of living.

Materials

Necessary materials will be found at each station.

Station 1: A Simple Generator
Observe the galvanometer as you quickly insert the magnet into the coil. What happens as the magnet enters the coil?

The galvanometer deflects momentarily, indicating the presence of a

transient electric current.

What happens once the magnet stops moving?

The galvanometer reads zero, indicating that there is no longer a current in

the coil.

Now quickly remove the magnet from the coil. What happens?

The galvanometer once again deflects, but in the opposite direction.

Time to Set Up: <1 h
Time in Lab: 1 h
Qualitative Lab

Equipment
Galvanometer, small coil of 30 turns of wire, bar magnet, two electrical leads

Slowly insert the magnet into the coil. Compare the galvanometer's response to the slowly moving magnet with its response to a rapidly moving magnet.

The galvanometer's deflection is less than when the magnet is inserted quickly.

Holding the magnet stationary, move the coil toward the magnet. Describe the behavior of the galvanometer while the coil is moving.

The galvanometer deflects momentarily, indicating the presence of a

transient electric current.

While the magnet is stationary, move the coil away from the magnet. Describe the behavior of the galvanometer while the coil is moving.

The galvanometer once again deflects, but in the opposite direction.

Summarize the results of this activity.

Whenever the magnetic field in the region of the coil is changing, an

electric current is produced.

Station 2: Electromagnetically Coupled Coils

Equipment
Audio source (i.e., radio or MP3 player), amplifier/speaker (available at RadioShack), electrical leads, two solenoids

Assembly
Use electrical leads to connect one solenoid to the audio source and the other solenoid to the amplifier/speaker.

Turn on the audio source and the amplifier/speaker. With the two coils parallel to each other, move one of the coils toward the other. What happens as the distance between the two coils decreases?

Sound is heard coming from the speaker.

How does the signal from the audio source reach the amplifier/speaker?

The fluctuating current from the audio source creates a changing magnetic

field in the coil connected to it. The changing magnetic field induces a

voltage in the coil connected to the amplifier/speaker. This voltage causes a

current in the second coil. This current is amplified and sent to the speaker,

where sound is produced.

What happens when you rotate one of the coils through 90°? Why do you think this occurs?

The sound becomes softer or may no longer be heard. Rotating the coil

through 90° eliminates the flux through the second coil.

Station 3: Pumping a Ring

Equipment
Coil of wire of approximately 50 turns, bar magnet, ringstand, clamp, insulating rod, connecting wire with alligator clips

Describe what happens when you rapidly insert one end of the bar magnet into the suspended coil of wire.

The coil moves away from the magnet.

Explain the behavior of the coil.

A current is induced in the coil, which turns the coil into an electromagnet.

The electromagnet is repelled by the bar magnet.

Once the coil is in motion, continue inserting and removing the magnet, adjusting your rate of motion so that the amplitude of the swings increases. How should the frequency of your "pumping" compare to the natural frequency of the hanging coil?

They should be equal.

Disconnect the wire connecting the ends of the coil. Once again, insert the magnet into the coil. What happens now?

The coil remains stationary.

Station 4: Magnetic Braking

Drop the piece of chalk into the tube. Now drop the magnet into the tube. Compare the motion of the two objects through the tube.

The unmagnetized object falls at a normal rate. The magnet descends very

slowly.

Equipment
Strong magnet (e.g., neodymium), piece of chalk approximately the same size as the magnet, copper pipe, PVC pipe with approximately the same dimensions as the copper pipe

Propose an explanation for the motion of the two objects.

The falling magnet induces eddy currents in the pipe. These currents

produce a magnetic field that opposes the motion of the magnet. The

unmagnetized object does not set up eddy currents in the pipe.

Repeat the experiment but, this time, use a nonmetallic tube (e.g., PVC pipe) with dimensions similar to those of the copper tube. Describe what happens this time. How do you explain the motion of the two objects now?

The tube is nonconducting and, as a result, both objects fall at essentially

the same rate.

Station 5: A Simple Linear Motor

While your lab partner holds the card by the edge with the magnet near the coil, touch the free ends of the electrical leads to the battery terminals. What happens?

The card is attracted to or repelled by the magnet, depending on the

direction of the current.

Equipment
Enameled magnet wire, 9 V battery, two electrical leads, radio or MP3 player

Assembly
Use an enameled magnet wire to make a coil with 30 turns and a 3 cm diameter. Using adhesive tape, attach the coil to a small sheet of posterboard. Remove the enamel from the ends of the coil and connect them to the two electrical leads.

While your lab partner continues to hold the magnet near the coil, reverse the leads and once again touch them to the battery terminals.

The card is attracted to or repelled by the magnet, depending on the

direction of the current.

Using the audio cable, connect the coil to an audio source. What do you hear when you bring the magnet near the coil? Why do you think this happens?

Sound is heard. The coil is alternately attracted and repelled by the magnet

in step with the fluctuating signal from the audio source.

Station 6: Motor-Generator Effect

Turn the crank of one of the generators by hand and observe the crank of the other generator. Now reverse the roles of the two devices. Is it clear which device is a motor and which is a generator? Explain your answer.

Simple DC motors and generators both have permanent magnets and coils

of wire, and thus a motor can function as a generator, and vice versa.

Equipment
Two hand-powered generators, two electrical leads

Assembly
Use the leads to connect the terminals of the two generators. If hand-powered generators are not available, you may use two small DC motors.

Chapter 23 Lab   Direction of Earth's Magnetic Field

Your Task

In this lab, you must determine the orientation of the earth's magnetic field.

Time to Set Up: <1 h
Time in Lab: 1 h
Performance Assessment

Equipment Provided

- a long extension cord
- wires with alligator clips
- galvanometer

You may not use a compass!

Requirements

- You must design an experiment to solve the problem.
- You may request additional equipment from your instructor.
- You will submit an equipment list and procedure before taking any data.
- You will only get one chance to ask for equipment. Make sure your list is complete.
- Your procedure should be thorough enough that another student in the class could follow your instructions.
- Present your data in tables, if appropriate.
- Show calculations used to solve the problem, if applicable.
- List at least two sources of error. For each, indicate what effect the error would have on your results.

Materials Requested

Students may ask for a magnetic field probe or a bar magnet.

_____

_____

_____

_____

_____

Procedure Followed

If students spin the extension cord like a jump rope, the galvanometer needle will move, indicating that an emf was induced on the cord. The galvanometer will move the most when students position the cord so it is perpendicular to the earth's magnetic field.

_____

_____

_____

_____

_____

_____

Data

Conclusion

_____

_____

_____

_____

Sources of Error

Possible sources of error include:

• Students will need to maintain the same rotational speed each time they rotate the cord.

• Students must keep the same distance between themselves for each trial.

• It may be difficult to tell the precise direction of the cord at which the motion is a maximum.

Name _____ Period _____ Date _____

Chapter 24 Lab   Determining Planck's Constant Using Light Emitting Diodes

Purpose

In this lab, you will use light emitting diodes (LEDs) to determine the value of Planck's constant.

Discussion

An LED is a solid-state light source consisting of two specially treated semiconducting materials (*n*-type and *p*-type) placed back to back. The *n*-type material has an excess of electrons; the *p*-type, a deficiency of electrons. When a potential difference, or voltage, applied to the sandwiched materials exceeds a threshold value V, electrons move from the *n*-type material to the *p*-type material. In the process they drop to a lower energy state, releasing energy in the form of photons of light.

In this experiment you will use a diffraction grating to determine the wavelength of light produced by LEDs of different colors and, for each LED, the threshold voltage needed to produce the light. Using this voltage, you will calculate the amount of energy converted to light as a result of the electron transition. The energy lost by each electron is given by eV, where e is the charge on the electron (1.6×10^{-19} C) and V is the voltage across the LED. This energy is equal to the energy hf of the emitted photons, where h is Planck's constant and f is the frequency of the emitted light. That is, $eV = hf$. Because $f = c/\lambda$, where $c = 3 \times 10^8$ m/s, $eV = hc/\lambda$. Therefore,

$$h = eV\lambda/c$$

Materials

- variable power supply
- red, green, yellow, and blue LEDs
- digital multimeter with leads
- diffraction grating
- two connecting leads with alligator clips
- two test-tube clamps
- two ringstands
- two meter sticks
- masking tape
- viewing tube

Time to Set Up: <1 h
Time in Lab> 1 h
Quantitative Lab

The activities in this laboratory should be performed in a darkened room. However, low-intensity lighting should be maintained to ensure safety of students as they move around.

Use construction paper and tape to form a cylindrical straw-like viewing tube with a diameter just slightly larger than that of the LEDs. The length of the tube may range from 5 to 10 cm. The viewing tube is used to best determine when the LED just begins to emit light.

Procedure ⚠

Part A: Measuring the Wavelength of Light Produced by LEDs

1. Obtain the grating spacing for your diffraction grating from your instructor and record it as d in the Data section.

2. Use a test-tube clamp and ringstand to support a meter stick. Position the meter stick so that the 50 cm mark is in the center of the test-tube clamp.

3. Use masking tape to secure the red LED to the meter stick at the 50 cm mark. Do not cover the upper, light-emitting portion of the LED with tape.

4. Use the second test-tube clamp and ringstand to serve as a support for the diffraction grating.

5. Align the grating so that it is parallel to the meter stick.

6. Position the grating so that the distance between the grating and the meter stick is 50 cm. Record the distance between the grating and the center of the meter stick as L in the data section.

7. With the power supply turned off, connect the LED to the DC output of the power supply using two connecting wires with alligator clips. The longer lead on the LED should be connected to the positive terminal on the power supply.

8. With the power supply voltage control at the zero position, turn on the power supply. Gradually increase the voltage until the LED produces light. Do not exceed 2.5 volts.

9. With the room lights off, look at the LED through the grating. In addition to the central diffraction image, you should see diffraction images on the meter stick to the right and left of center. These diffraction images will have some angular spread because the light emitted by the LED consists of a distribution of wavelengths.

10. While you continue to look at the LED through the grating, have a lab partner move a pencil along the meter stick until the pencil appears to you to be in the center of the first-order maximum to the right of the central maximum. Record this position as x_1 in Data Table 1.

11. Repeat step 10 for the first-order maximum on the left of the central maximum. Record this image position as x_2.

12. Switch roles with your partner and repeat the measurements. Continue alternating roles until four trials have been performed.

13. Repeat the steps above for the green, yellow, and blue LED light. Enter the data for each LED in the appropriate data table.

In this section of the lab, students will need to make the LED bright enough so that they can see the diffraction pattern. To prevent damage to the LEDs, voltage should not exceed 2.5 V.

To check the accuracy of results, the typical wavelength for each LED is printed on the packaging it came in.

Part B: Determining Threshold Voltage

1. With the power supply turned off and the red LED connected to the DC output of the power supply, attach the leads of the multimeter to the terminals of the power supply. Make certain that the + and − multimeter leads are attached to the appropriate power supply terminals.

2. Place the viewing tube over the LED and turn off the room lights.

3. With the power supply voltage control at the zero position, turn on the power supply. Gradually increase the voltage until the LED just begins to produce light. This voltage is the threshold voltage. Read the multimeter to determine the voltage. Record this in Data Table 5.

4. Repeat steps 1—3 for each of the remaining LEDs.

Data

$L =$ _____ m $d =$ _____ m

Data Table 1: Red LED			
Trial	x_1 (m)	x_2 (m)	Δx (m)
1			
2			
3			
4			
Average			

Data Table 2: Green LED			
Trial	x_1 (m)	x_2 (m)	Δx (m)
1			
2			
3			
4			
Average			

Data Table 3: Yellow LED			
Trial	x_1 (m)	x_2 (m)	Δx (m)
1			
2			
3			
4			
Average			

Data Table 4: Blue LED			
Trial	x_1 (m)	x_2 (m)	Δx (m)
1			
2			
3			
4			
Average			

Data Table 5	
LED color	**Measured threshold voltage (V)**
Red	
Green	
Yellow	
Blue	

Table 6						
LED color	**Average Δx(m)**	**tan θ**	**θ**	**sin θ**	**λ(m)**	**h (J s)**
Red						
Green						
Yellow						
Blue						

Average calculated value of Planck's constant: _____ J s

Analysis

1. Calculate the average of the four measured values of Δx for each of the four LEDs. Enter these values in Table 6.

2. Use the average value of Δx for each LED to calculate tan θ, using $\tan \theta = \Delta x / L$. Enter these values in Table 6.

3. Determine θ for each LED by applying the inverse tangent function. Enter these values in Table 6.

4. Determine sin θ for each LED. Enter these values in Table 6.

5. Apply $d \sin \theta = m\lambda$ to find the wavelength of each LED. Enter these values in Table 6.

6. Use $h = eV\lambda/c$ to determine the value of Planck's constant. Enter these values in Table 6.

Questions

1. Find the accepted value of Planck's constant in your textbook. Calculate your percent error using the accepted value and your average calculated value.
   Expect errors of 15–20%.

2. What are some of the sources of error in your measurements?
   Error may be introduced when measuring the lengths associated with finding wavelengths and determining the centers of the spread-out diffraction images. Determining when an LED just begins to glow can introduce error.

Chapter 25: Atomic Physics • **Fluorescence and Phosphorescence**

Chapter 25 Lab   Exploring Fluorescence and Phosphorescence

Purpose
In this lab, you will investigate the phenomena of fluorescence and phosphorescence.

Materials
Necessary materials will be found at each station.

Discussion
Fluorescence is a phenomenon that occurs when a substance gives off visible light after absorbing electromagnetic radiation that is not normally visible, such as ultraviolet light. When an atom absorbs radiation, its electrons become excited and move to higher energy states. With fluorescence the electrons in an atom return to their lowest energy states in stages. Instead of returning to their ground state in one fell swoop, the electrons drop via intermediate excited states. This multiple-step decay process results in a number of photons, or bundles of light, each with a fraction of the energy of the photon that was absorbed.

When the time required for an electron to return to a lower energy state is relatively long, the emission of light is called phosphorescence. Thus the principal difference between fluorescence and phosphorescence is the time required for light emission. Some definitions of phosphorescence require that the emission delay be only 10 nanoseconds (10^{-8} s). However, when most people think of phosphorescence, they think of an object glowing for minutes or even hours.

Procedure ⚠

Station 1: Analyzing Light Produced by a Fluorescent Lamp
Shine the fluorescent light on the blades of the fan. Study the blades very closely for various rates of rotation. What do you observe about the colors you see for certain blade speeds? Why do you think this occurs?

Light coloration will be seen on the blades for certain rates of rotation.

The fluorescent tube is coated with a variety of phosphors, each of which

produces a different color. *Note:* The effect is very subtle.

Time to Set Up: <1 h
Time in Lab: 1 h
Qualitative Lab

Phosphorescent film or paper may be obtained from science supply companies. The activities in this laboratory should be performed in a darkened room. However, low-intensity lighting should be maintained to ensure the safety of students as they move around.

Equipment
Standard fluorescent lamp, electric fan with white blades

Equipment
Clear plastic objects, such as clear, colored (orange, yellow, or green) cups and clipboards, tonic water, toothpaste, white computer paper, a black light

Station 2: Household Fluorescence

Describe the appearance of the objects at this station when the "black light" is used to illuminate them. Why do the objects appear as they do under black light?

The objects have a vibrant "neon" appearance. Fluorescent dyes in many

common products produce this effect. The electrons in the dyes are excited by

the black light. These dyes are used to make the objects appear more vibrant.

Equipment
Small dish, laundry detergent, water, cotton swabs, white paper, black light

Assembly
Prepare a dilute solution of detergent and water. You may want to test the laundry deter-gent solution for the desired effect.

Station 3: Invisible Writing

After dipping the end of a cotton swab in the detergent solution, use the swab to write a message or produce a drawing on a sheet of white paper. Describe what you see.

When dry, the writing or artwork should be invisible.

What do you observe when you use the black light to illuminate the paper?

The writing or artwork will become visible.

Why does black light produce this result?

Many laundry detergents contain fluorescent dyes. When illuminated with

ultraviolet light they give off a cool blue light.

Equipment
Sheet of phosphorescent film, camera flash or other bright light source
For best results the phos-phorescent film should be kept out of direct light prior to use.

Station 4: Shadow Formation

Place your hand on the photosensitive side of a sheet of phosphorescent film. Illuminate your hand and film with a camera flash or other bright light. Describe the film after the light source ceases to shine on it.

The film glows green after the light ceases to shine on it.

Now remove your hand and observe the phosphorescent film. What do you observe? Explain your observation.

A shadow of the hand is seen on the film. The area beneath the hand was

not exposed to light.

Equipment
Sheet of phosphorescent film, camera flash, small fan

Station 5: Stop-Action Image

Place the fan between a sheet of phosphorescent film and the flash unit. With the fan blades spinning, actuate the flash. Describe the resulting shadow on the film.

A relatively sharp image of the blades is seen on the film.

Equipment
Black light or bright white light source, sheet of phosphores-cent film, ice cube, plastic bag or plastic wrap

Station 6: Temperature and Phosphorescence

Wrap an ice cube with plastic. Expose the film to a source of bright light. Place the wrapped ice cube on the phosphorescent film and turn off the light source. After four or five minutes, remove the ice cube and compare

Name _____ Period _____ Date _____

the relative brightness of the region of the film that was beneath the ice to its surroundings. What do you observe?

The area that was beneath the ice cube appears less bright than the

surroundings.

What does this indicate about the rate at which light is given off by the phosphorescent material in the two regions?

The rate of light emission is less in the cooled region.

Why do you think the rate of light emission is affected by the lower temperature?

The motion of molecules making up the film causes electrons to fall back to

their normal energy levels at a faster rate. Molecular motion is reduced by

cooling, which reduces the rate of light emission.

Continue watching the film for several minutes. What changes in brightness do you observe as time passes? Can you explain what is going on?

The area that was beneath the ice becomes brighter than the surroundings.

There are more excited atoms remaining in that area than in its surroundings.

Station 7: Color and Phosphorescence

Place the six colored filters on the surface of the phosphorescent film. It is not necessary that the filters completely cover the phosphorescent film, but the filters should not overlap. Illuminate the filter-covered phosphorescent film with bright light. After the light is turned off, remove the six filters and examine the film. Explain the regions of relative light and dark you see on the film. It may help to remember that a yellow filter passes both red and green light, a cyan filter passes both green and blue light, and a magenta filter passes both red and blue light.

If the light that reaches the film is less energetic than green light, there will

be insufficient energy to produce phosphorescence. Thus red light will not

be able to "charge" the phosphorescent film, but green and blue light will.

Use the red and green and lasers to write your name on the phosphorescent paper. DO NOT SHINE THE LASERS IN ANYONE'S EYES. Which lasers produce phosphorescence? Explain.

Red light will not be able to "charge" the phosphorescent film, but green

light will.

Station 8: Glow and Afterglow

Turn on the television. Once the screen is filled with light, turn the television off. Now closely examine the screen. What do you see? With the television turned off, illuminate the screen with the flash from a

Equipment
Phosphorescent film, bright light source, colored filters (red, blue, green, cyan, magenta, yellow), red and green laser pointers

Safety
Students should never look into a direct or reflected laser beam.

Equipment
Old style television or computer monitor (CRT, not flat screen), camera flash or black light

Pearson Physics Lab Manual • Copyright © Pearson Education, Inc., or its affiliates. All rights reserved.

265

camera or light from a black light. What do you see when the source of illumination is removed?

The light seen while the television is on is due to fluorescing phosphors.

If the room is sufficiently dark, a dim phosphorescent afterglow will be

seen after the television has been turned off or after the screen has been

illuminated.

Chapter 26: Nuclear Physics • **Radioactivity**

Chapter 26 Lab   Detecting Radioactivity

Purpose

In this lab, you will learn how to detect and measure radioactivity and observe how the levels of alpha, beta, and gamma radiation are affected by (1) the distance between source and detector and (2) shielding.

Discussion

When nuclear disintegration takes place, several types of radiation may be emitted, alpha (α), beta (β), and gamma (γ) radiation being the most common. Positively charged α particles, consisting of two protons and two neutrons, have relatively large mass and interact strongly with matter. Negatively charged β particles, which are fast-moving electrons, have a much smaller mass. They interact less with matter than do α particles. The third type of radiation is γ rays, which are not particles but very high-energy photons. They interact with matter much less strongly than do α and β particles.

The presence of radiation is detected by the ionization that it produces. Devices used to detect radiation include cloud and bubble chambers, scintillation counters, semiconducting detectors, and, perhaps the most well known, the Geiger counter.

At the heart of a Geiger counter is a gas-filled glass tube. At the end of the tube is a mica window that allows passage of incident radiation. Within the tube are two electrodes: a negatively charged cylinder (the cathode) and a positively charged wire (the anode) running down the cylinder's center. A potential difference, slightly less than that needed to ionize the gas, is maintained between the cathode and anode. Ionizing radiation entering the tube produces electrons and ions. The electrons are attracted toward the anode while the positively charged ions move toward the cathode. As these particles move, they collide with the remaining gas molecules, producing an avalanche of additional charged particles. This rush of charged particles constitutes a current, which, after amplification, is displayed on a meter or made audible.

Materials

- Geiger counter
- sources of alpha, beta, and gamma radiation
- sheets of paper
- sheets of aluminum foil

Time to Set Up: <1 h
Time in Lab: 1 h
Quantitative Lab

Safety
Radioactive materials should be handled with care. Students should wear goggles and use tweezers, tongs, or gloves to manipulate the radioactive sources. Food and drink should not be consumed, nor should anything be placed in the mouth while performing this experiment. It is essential that students wash their hands at the conclusion of the experiment.

- sheet of lead
- meter stick

Procedure 🔬 🖐 🔥

Part A: Determining the Background Radiation

Background radiation is radiation emitted by natural and artificial sources and is constantly present in the earth's natural environment. With the three sources kept far away, use the Geiger counter to measure the background radiation. Each trial should last 30 seconds. Repeat this two more times and record the results in Data Table 1.

Part B: Effect of Distance on Intensity of Radiation

1. Place the gamma ray source 5 cm from the Geiger counter and measure the count rate for 30 seconds. Perform four additional trials and record results in Data Table 2.

2. Repeat step 1 for distances of 10 and 15 cm.

Part C: Effect of Shielding on Intensity of Radiation

Perform each of these experiments three times.

1. Place the alpha source at a distance of 1 cm from the Geiger counter. Measure the count rate for 30 seconds. Record the count rate in Data Table 3.

2. Place a sheet of paper between the source and the counter. Measure the count rate for 30 seconds. Record the count rate in Data Table 3.

3. Repeat steps 1 and 2 using a sheet of aluminum foil as the shield.

4. Repeat steps 1 and 2 using a sheet of lead as the shield.

5. Repeat steps 1–4 using the beta source.

6. Repeat steps 1–4 using the gamma source.

Data

Data Table 1	
Trial	**Background count rate (counts/30 sec)**
1	
2	
3	
Average	

Data Table 2

Distance between source and counter (cm)	Gamma count rate (counts/30 sec)	Gamma count rate (counts/30 sec)	Gamma count rate (counts/30 sec)	Gamma count rate (counts/30 sec)	Gamma count rate (counts/30 sec)	Average gamma count rate (counts/30 sec)
5						
10						
15						

Data Table 3

Shielding material	Type of particle	Count rate trial 1 (counts/30 sec)	Count rate trial 2 (counts/30 sec)	Count rate trial 3 (counts/30 sec)	Average count rate (counts/30 sec)
none	alpha				
none	beta				
none	gamma				
paper	alpha				
paper	beta				
paper	gamma				
aluminum	alpha				
aluminum	beta				
aluminum	gamma				
lead	alpha				
lead	beta				
lead	gamma				

Table 4

Distance between source and counter (cm)	Gamma count rate minus background (counts/min)
5	
10	
15	

Table 5		
Shielding material	Type of particle	Average count rate minus background (counts/30 sec)
none	alpha	
none	beta	
none	gamma	
paper	alpha	
paper	beta	
paper	gamma	
aluminum	alpha	
aluminum	beta	
aluminum	gamma	
lead	alpha	
lead	beta	
lead	gamma	

Analysis

1. Find the average count per 30 seconds for each trial in Data Tables 1, 2, and 3.

2. Calculate and record the average count rates minus average background in Tables 4 and 5.

Conclusions

1. Why does the background radiation need to be subtracted from all other measurements?

   To obtain a true count rate for a radioactive source, the background

   radiation, which is always present, must be subtracted from the count

   rate obtained from the radioactive source.

2. What effect does increasing the distance from a radioactive source have on the count rate?

   The count rate decreases with increasing distance.

3. Which sample had the most intense radiation?

Answers will vary.

4. Describe the best way to shield against each of the three types of radiation.

Alpha radiation may be stopped by a few centimeters of air or a thin

sheet of paper. Beta particles can be blocked by aluminum or plastic. If

sufficiently thick, lead may be used to stop most gamma radiation.

Chapter 26 Lab Elementary Particle Tracks in a Cloud Chamber

Purpose

In this lab, you will construct a cloud chamber. You will then use the device to view the tracks produced by radioactive decay by-products from sources such as cosmic rays, the earth's crust, and a sample of radioactive material.

Time to Set Up: <1 h
Time in Lab: 1 h
Qualitative Lab

Discussion

A cloud chamber is a device used to reveal the presence of charged subatomic particles. While it is not possible to see the particles themselves, it is possible to see the vapor trails they produce as they move through the chamber.

A simple, continuously operating cloud chamber, called a diffusion cloud chamber, consists of a transparent closed container that is very cold at the bottom and warm at the top. An absorbent material, such as felt, soaked with alcohol lines the top or interior wall of the container. As the alcohol vaporizes, it drifts slowly downward and, in a region near the bottom, becomes supersaturated. The process of condensation of the supersaturated vapor into liquid can be triggered by the passage of a charged particle with enough energy to ionize atoms in its path. The ionized atoms serve as condensation nuclei around which liquid droplets form. These droplets appear as tracks in the illuminated container.

Different types of particles will leave different trails. The length of the track depends on the particle's energy and mass. Alpha particles, which are relatively heavy, usually produce broad, straight trails. Beta particles (electrons) leave long, thin tracks. Muons, particles with the same charge as an electron but 200 times more massive, are constantly being produced as cosmic rays—protons, for example—bombard gas molecules in the atmosphere. Muons produce a well-defined straight track. Tracks that begin straight and then suddenly veer sharply to the right or left result from the decay of a muon.

Materials

- petri dish with a lid
- felt
- black construction paper
- 91% isopropyl alcohol
- dry ice
- flashlight
- thermal gloves
- radioactive sample

If your school doesn't have any radioactive sources, you can use gas lamp mantles such as those found in gas-burning camping lamps. The thorium oxide used to coat some of the mantles is a natural alpha particle emitter. Many brands of replacement mantles found in stores (e.g., Coleman) no longer contain thorium oxide; however, radioactive mantles may be purchased from many science supply companies.

Safety

Students should wear goggles throughout this experiment. They should also always wear thermal gloves while handling dry ice. Isopropyl alcohol is flammable, so it should not be used near an open flame or anything that is hot. The area in which this experiment is performed should be well ventilated. Radioactive materials should be handled with care. Most sources used in schools, including thorium oxide, are safe if they are handled properly and not ingested.

Procedure

1. Use the bottom of the petri dish to draw a circle on the construction paper.

2. Cut the circular disk out of construction paper and trim it so that it will fit inside the bottom of the petri dish.

3. Place the construction paper disk on the inside bottom of the petri dish.

4. Prepare a strip of felt so that it will completely cover the interior wall of the petri dish.

5. Use glue or other adhesive to attach the felt strip to the inside wall of the petri dish.

6. After the glue has dried, thoroughly soak the felt with isopropyl alcohol. Do not be concerned if some alcohol gets on the construction paper.

7. After placing the lid on the petri dish, warm the dish by holding it between the palms of your hands for a minute or two.

8. Place the petri dish on the dry ice with the bottom of the petri dish in contact with the ice. In a darkened room, illuminate the petri dish with the flashlight. In a few minutes you should observe the formation of particle tracks. Observe the cloud chamber for several minutes and draw examples of tracks you see in the cloud chamber in Data Circle 1.

9. Insert the radioactive sample in the cloud chamber. Once again, observe the tracks produced. Draw examples of the tracks observed in Data Circle 2.

Data

Data Circle 1

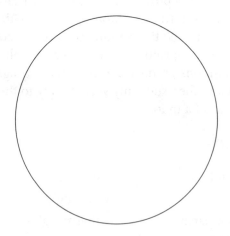

Data Circle 2

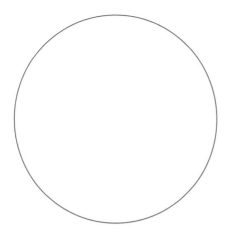

Analysis and Conclusions

1. Based on your observations, what types of particles observed are naturally occurring: that is, which come from cosmic rays, the earth, or nearby radioactive objects?

Answers will vary. _____

_____

_____

2. What types of particles were emitted by the radioactive source placed in the cloud chamber?

Answers will vary. _____

_____

_____

There are no labs for Chapter 27.

There are no labs for Chapter 27.